Electrical Installations

Illustrated Dictionary

John Blaus

www.harcourt.co.uk

✓ Free online support
✓ Useful weblinks
✓ 24 hour online ordering

01865 888058

From Harcourt

Heinemann Educational Publishers
Halley Court, Jordan Hill, Oxford OX2 8EJ
Part of Harcourt Education

Heinemann is the registered trademark of Harcourt Education Limited.

First published 2007

10 09 08 07
10 9 8 7 6 5 4 3 2 1

British Library Cataloguing in Publication Data is available from the British Library on request.

10-digit ISBN: 0435402072
13-digit ISBN: 978 0 435402075

Edited by Alexander Gray
Designed by HL Studios, Long Hanborough
Typeset by HL Studios, Long Hanborough

Illustrated by HL Studios, Long Hanborough
Cover design by GD Associates
Printed in the UK by Scotprint

Picture research by Chrissie Martin

Tel: 01865 888058 www.heinemann.co.uk

Introduction

This book has been designed as an essential reference tool for trainees, apprentices and experienced electrical installation professionals, providing quick and clear guidance on key electrotechnical terms and processes.

The dictionary contains over 1,000 entries, covering the full range of work activities undertaken in the electrotechnical industry.

Each entry in this practical, easy-to-use dictionary, clearly defines the meaning, application and purpose of the term. The many full-colour photographs and illustrations provide further clarity and essential information about complex components and procedures.

Cross-references to other entries in the dictionary are identified in *red italics* the first time they appear in a definition aiding your research on a particular subject. Entries that are described by multiple terms such as 'cable', 'generator' or 'motor' are fully cross-referenced.

So, whether you are just starting out on a career in the electrotechnical sector or have been working in the industry for some time, the Electrical Installations Illustrated Dictionary is your key reference to obtaining a clear, concise and current interpretation of the many terms that are used by the electrotechnical industry.

John Blaus

Acknowledgements

The author and publisher would like to thank the following individuals and organisations for permission to reproduce photographs:

Alamy Images pages 138, 148; **Corbis/Roger Ressmeyer** page 48; **Getty Images/ PhotoDisc** page 56; **Ginny Stroud-Lewis** page 95; **Harcourt Education Ltd/ Gareth Boden** pages 12, 13, 16, 26, 36, 41, 60, 66, 83, 93, 97, 116, 117, 119, 122; **Science Photo Library/Andrew Lanbert Photography** page 2; **Science Photo Library/Cordelia Molloy** page 145

The publisher would like to thank Sue Meredith, for her extensive development work on the early draft of this manuscript and Brian Clements and Andy Thirtle for their invaluable comments.

a.c. (alternating current)

The flow of electrons, which rises to a maximum value in one direction then falls back to zero before rising to a maximum value in the opposite direction.

a.c. circuit cable colour

The insulation of cables is coloured to identify the type of cable, in accordance with BS 7671.

Function	Colour
Protective conductors	Green and yellow
Functional earthing conductor	Cream
a.c. power circuit[1] Phase of single-phase circuit Neutral of single- or three-phase circuit Phase 1 of three-phase a.c. circuit Phase 2 of three-phase a.c. circuit Phase 3 of three-phase a.c. circuit	 Brown Blue Brown Black Grey
Two-wire unearthed d.c. power circuit Positive of two-wire circuit Negative of two-wire circuit	 Brown Grey
Two-wire earthed d.c. power circuit Positive (of negative earthed) circuit Negative (of negative earthed) circuit	 Brown Blue
Positive (of positive earthed) circuit Negative (of positive earthed) circuit	Blue Grey

▲ Identifying cable insulation in accordance with BS 7671 *(continued)*

Function	Colour
Three-wire d.c. power circuit Outer positive of two-wire circuit derived from three-wire system Outer negative of two-wire circuit derived from three-wire system Positive of three-wire circuit Mid-wire of three-wire circuit[2] Negative of three-wire circuit	 Brown Grey Brown Blue Grey
Control circuits, ELV and other applications Phase conductor	Brown, black, red, orange, yellow, violet, grey, white, pink or turquoise
Neutral or mid-wire[3]	Blue

NOTES
(1) Power circuits include lighting circuits.
(2) Only the middle wire of three-wire circuits may be earthed.
(3) An earthed PELV conductor is blue.

▲ Identifying cable insulation in accordance with BS 7671

a.c. drive

A variable frequency inverter unit, often called a variable frequency drive (VFD). The motor is a separate component.

See *Variable frequency drive (VFD)*

a.c. generator

A generator or alternator which produces an alternating current. The a.c. generator usually has a stationary armature, or *stator*, and a rotating *magnetic field*, or *rotor*.

In its simplest form, a looped conductor is mounted so that it can rotate between two permanent magnets. As the loop rotates it cuts through the lines of flux and induces an *e.m.f.* When the loop moves through 90° the peak value of induced e.m.f. in the first direction is reached. As the loop continues to rotate, the number of flux lines cut reduces to zero. The loop has completed the positive half-cycle. When the process is repeated an e.m.f. is induced in the opposite direction (the negative half-cycle). The

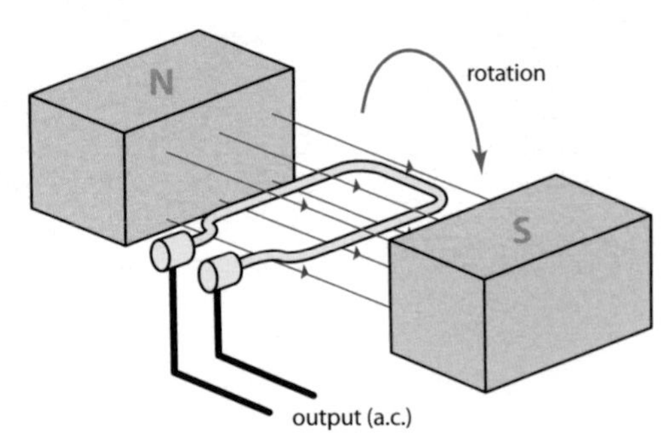

▲ An a.c. generator

opposite directions of the induced e.m.f. drive an alternating current through a conductor. The ends of the loop are connected with slip rings to enable the current to flow through an external circuit. The number of cycles per second is the frequency, measured in hertz (Hz). In the UK, the frequency is 50 Hz.

a.c. motor

A means of converting electric power to mechanical power. The a.c. produces a rotating magnetic field. A conductor placed within this rotating field will also rotate. A metal armature will rotate with very little slippage and a shaft attached to the armature will deliver mechanical power to, for example, a fan or a water pump. The a.c. motor operates through the changing polarity of the current running through the *stator*. The a.c. induction motor relies on the *rotor* attempting to catch up with the stator's magnetic field.

See *Capacitor start-capacitor run motor; Capacitor-start induction run motor; Induction motor; Series motor; Shaded pole motor; Single-phase a.c. synchronous induction motor; Single-phase motor; Split-phase motor; Squirrel cage motor; synchronous a.c. induction motor; Three-phase induction motor*

▲ A simple a.c. motor

A
B
C
D
E
F
G
H
I
J
K
L
M
N
O
P
Q
R
S
T
U
V
W
X
Y
Z

active or true power

The power in a circuit which is used by the resistor(s). The apparent power in a resistive circuit is voltage (V) × current (I). The active or true power takes the phase angle (Ø) into account. It may be less than or equal to the apparent power and is calculated by the formula:

True power = VI cos Ø

See *Apparent power*; *Reactive power*

adiabatic equation

An equation used to work out whether a *conductor* can carry a fault current without overheating. Regulation 543-01-01 of the IEE Wiring *Regulations* states that 'The cross-sectional area of every protective conductor shall be calculated in accordance with Regulation 543-01-03 (adiabatic equation) or selected in accordance with Regulation 543-01-04 (Table 54G).' The adiabatic equation is used to check the suitability of the *circuit protective conductor* (cpc) in a multicore cable. If the cable does not incorporate a cpc, a cpc installed as a separate conductor may also be checked. Before using the adiabatic equation, the value of I (fault current) must be calculated using the equation:

$$I = \frac{U_O}{Z_S}$$

Where U_O is the nominal supply voltage to earth, and Z_S is the *earth fault loop impedance*. The adiabatic equation is:

$$S = \frac{\sqrt{I_{EF} \times t}}{k}$$

where:

S = the cross-sectional area of the cpc in mm^2

I_{EF} = the value of the fault current I for earth fault current

t = is the operating time of the disconnecting device in seconds

k = is a factor depending on the conductor and its insulating material

air pollution

Air contaminated by substances called pollutants, which are produced naturally or by human activity. Most pollution of the air by humans is through the burning of fossil fuels, such as coal, oil and gas (as in the case of power plants and motor vehicles) that release chemicals such as CO_2, nitrogen oxides and sulphur oxides into the air.

alarm and emergency installations

See *Fire alarm system*; *Intruder alarm system*

alternating waveform frequency

In alternating current generation, the number of cycles per second is the *frequency* of the waveform, measured in hertz (Hz) – the frequency of the UK a.c. supply is 50 Hz. If one cycle of *e.m.f.* is generated by one revolution in one second, the frequency would be 1 Hz. The frequency of the waveform is related to the speed of rotation, measured in revolutions per second. We can express this using the following equation:

Frequency (f) = Number of revolutions (n) × Number of *pole pairs*

ambient temperature

The temperature of the surroundings. For example, for a cable the ambient temperature is the temperature of the air in the room where the cable is installed. Cables generate heat when carrying *current* and so must be able to give heat off to the surrounding air. If the air itself is warm, the heat will not dissipate as quickly and the cable could heat up, with a risk of a fire. Cables must be selected using a correction factor for ambient temperature. Tables 4C1 and 4C2 of the IEE Wiring *Regulations* give cable selections based on an ambient temperature of 30°C. If the temperature is above 30°C the selection available is limited; below 30°C; the selection available is wider, as the heat will dissipate more quickly.

ammeter

An instrument used for measuring *current*. Ammeters should be connected in series in the circuit that measurements are being taken from.

ampere

A unit of current equal to the flow of one *coulomb* of charge per second.

analogue device

An instrument in which the measurements are shown by the position of a marker or pointer on a calibrated scale, as in a clock with hands.

antistatic precautions

These are precautions taken in areas containing flammable or explosive materials, such as petrol stations. Special induction training should be undertaken before working in these areas.

apparent power

The power in a *resistive circuit* that is equal to *voltage* (V) × *current* (I) is known as the apparent power. It has a *power factor* of one, the unity power factor. The *active or true power* may be equal to or less than the apparent power. Apparent power is measured in volt-amps (VA).

See *Reactive power; True or active power; Power factor*

A B C D E F G H I J K L M N O P Q R S T U V W X Y Z

arc tube

The glass tube in a *discharge* or *fluorescent* lamp, which is pressurised with argon or neon and has an electrode fitted at either end. A rare metal, such as mercury, may also be added to the arc tube.

armature

The moving part of an electrical machine in which a *voltage* is induced by a *magnetic field*.

See *Rotor*; *Stator*

asbestos dust safety

Asbestos is a mineral used in the making of fibrous materials used in insulation, floor and ceiling tiling, and fire-resistant board for doors and partitions. If materials containing asbestos are disturbed, the fibres may be freed and these, if inhaled, can cause a very serious long-term incurable illness, known as asbestosis. Make sure that you wear the correct personal protective equipment and follow Health and Safety procedures meticulously.

assembly drawing

An easy-to-follow diagram which shows how an item is assembled from the component parts. The diagram is usually drawn to scale, showing and describing each component.

The example shown here is the assembly drawing for a push-button enclosure.

A Enclosure base with built-in contact block clips
B Contact blocks/lamp holders
C Locking ring
D Enclosure lid
E Legend plate
F Captive screws (after screw in) loose in enclosure on delivery
G Actuators and lens cap

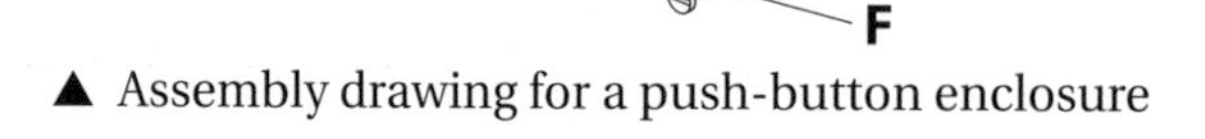

▲ Assembly drawing for a push-button enclosure

assumed current demand

This is the total current drawn by all circuits connected in an installation, after diversity has been allowed for, in accordance with the latest version of BS 7671.

asynchronous

This applies to motors where the speed of the rotating *magnetic field* is different from the speed of the motor.

automatic star-delta contactor starter

A motor starter which enables larger motors to start at a reduced voltage. This reduces the inrush current drawn by the motor on start-up by enabling the motor to start with the windings connected in the star configuration (230 volts) and then switching to the delta connection (400 volts) when indicated by a timer. The starter has three sets of contacts, one being the main contact and the other two used to connect the windings, firstly in star and then in delta. The change from star to delta is fully automated and the timings can be adjusted to suit the application. Care must be taken to ensure that the delta connection is not made too quickly, or *transient overload* could occur.

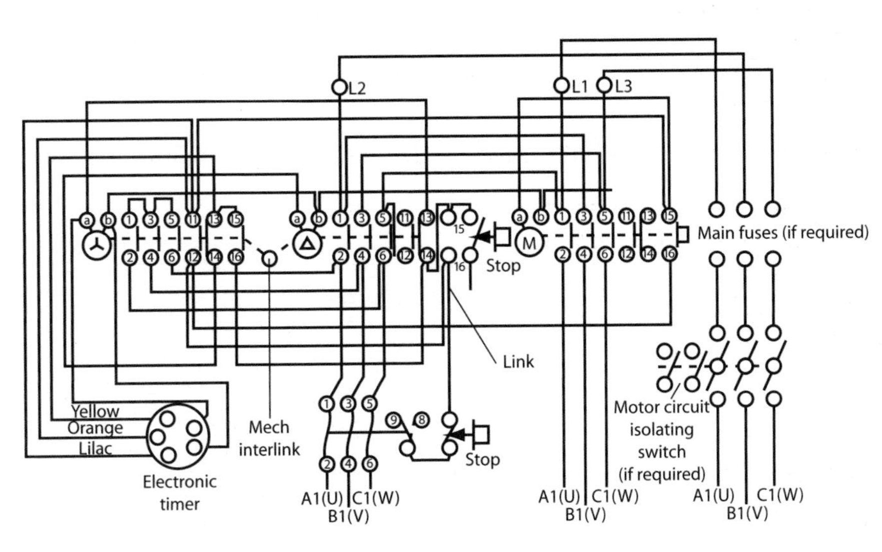

▲ Automatic star-delta contactor starter

autotransformer

This produces varying output voltage using one tapped winding. The position of the tapping controls the output voltage. The autotransformer will become hazardous if the winding is broken between the tapping points.

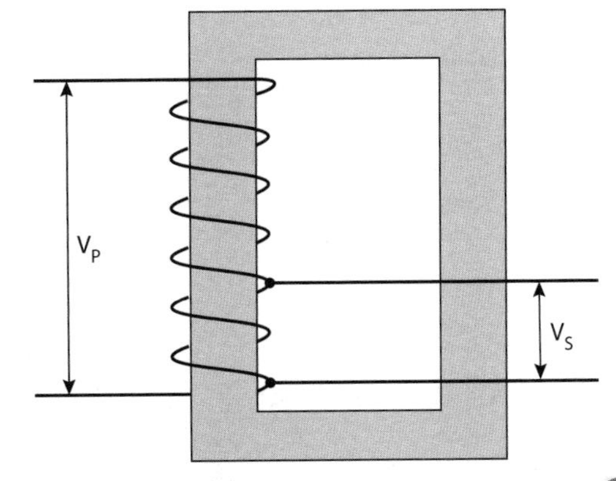

▲ Autotransformer

autotransformer starter

A starter method used when the starting *torque* must be high, or when the motor terminal box has only three terminals. A three-phase autotransformer has tapped windings designed to give 40 per cent, 60 per cent and 75 per cent of the *line voltage* respectively.

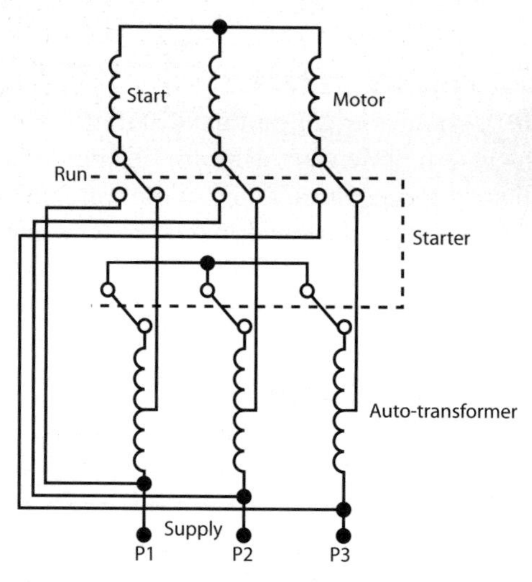

▲ Connections for an autotransformer starter

average value

This refers to the average of an alternating waveform over one half-cycle of the instantaneous values as they change from zero to maximum. The average value is calculated using the following formula:

$$V_{av} = 0.637 \times V_{max}$$

See *Sine wave*; *rms (root mean square)*; *a.c. (alternating current)*

ballast inductance/choke inductance

A coil used in *fluorescent lamps* to provide a high back *e.m.f.* which ionises the gas and causes the lamp to strike up. It also provides a secondary function as a current-limiting device.

bar chart

The graphical expression of data using bars. One type of bar chart, called a *Gantt chart*, is used on construction projects to show the schedule of activities. The main contractor can see from this chart when individual trade contractors are due on site.

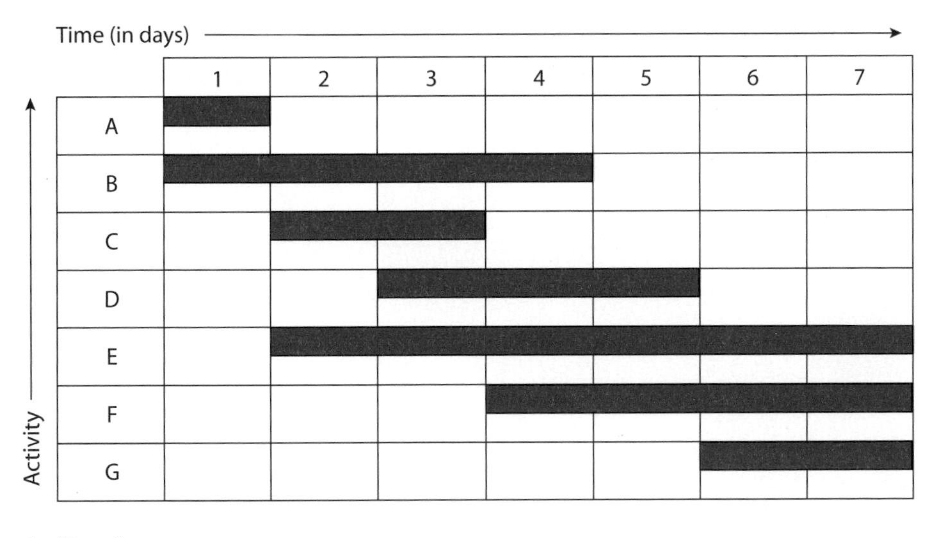

▲ Bar chart

A
B
C
D
E
F
G
H
I
J
K
L
M
N
O
P
Q
R
S
T
U
V
W
X
Y
Z

bath or shower locations

Electrical equipment locations with a bath or shower in the same room present a high risk of electric shock. Regulation 601 refers to four zones, zone 0 is the immediate area around the water supply and zones 1 to 3 are measured distances from zone 0. Refer to Section 6 in the IEE Wiring *Regulations*. Special requirements are listed in the Regulations for:

- protection against electric shock (refer to Regulation 601-03-02)
- supplementary equipotential bonding (refer to Regulation 601-04-01)
- protective measures against electric shock (refer to Regulation 601-05)
- wiring systems (refer to Regulation 601-07)
- switch gear and control gear (refer to Regulation 601-08)
- fixed current using equipment (refer to Regulation 601-09).

The Regulations also list some common rules and external influences (refer to Regulation 601-06-01).

battery

A battery has an internal chemical reaction that provides an *electromotive force (e.m.f.)* which forces electrons along the conducting wire and through the load connected to the battery, for example a lamp. The electrons pass through and heat the filament of the lamp and return back to the battery through the second conductor. Batteries are used to store electrical energy for backup supplies, and care should be taken especially with the lead acid type. These contain sulphuric acid, which is corrosive, and they also emit explosive hydrogen gas during the charging process.

See *Circuit (battery driven)*

bending conduit

Bends are made in *conduit* using a former or a bending machine. The different types of bend that can be made, and their application, are shown in the table.

Right-angled bend	This is used to go around a corner or change direction by 90°. When bending, measurements may be taken from the back, centre or front of the bend. Allowance should be made for the depth of the fixing saddle bases.	
Set	The set is used when surface levels change or when terminating into a box entry. Sets should be parallel and square, not too long, and not so short that the end cannot be threaded. Where there are numerous sets together all sets must be of the same length. The double set is used when passing girders or obstacles.	Set Double set

▲ Types of bend (continued)

Kick	The kick is used when a conduit run changes direction by less than 90°.	
Bubble set or saddle set	The bubble set or saddle set is used when passing obstructions, especially pipes or roof trusses etc. The centre of the obstruction should be central to the set.	

▲ Types of bend

bill of quantities (B of Q)

A document produced by a quantity surveyor by measuring or 'taking off' the quantities of materials from a drawing. The B of Q lists the amounts and costs of all the materials required for a contract and is used to control costs and provide milestones for contractors' payments.

bimetallic strip

Device in a *thermostat* consisting of two different metals, bonded together. The metals expand at different rates when heated causing the strip to bend, making or breaking an electrical contact and thus switching on or off the heating system controlled by the thermostat.

block diagram

A very simplified diagram showing the sequence of control for an installation.

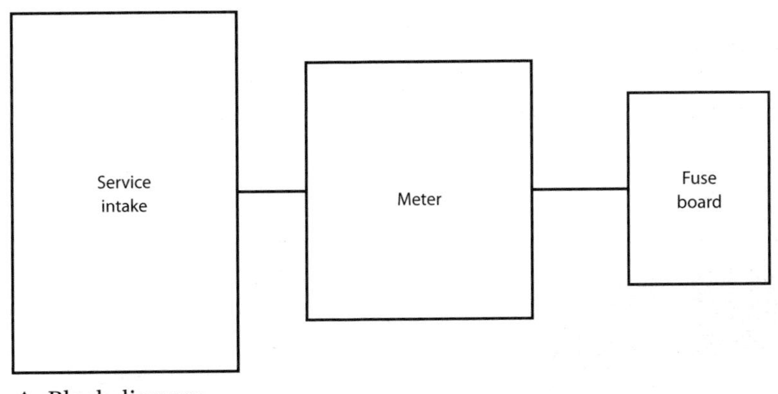

▲ Block diagram

British Standards

The British Standards Institution (BSI) sets quality standards and standard dimensions for equipment and materials. All British Standards start with the letters BS followed by a number, for example BS 6551 deals with protection of structures against lightning and BS 7671 is the 16th edition of the IEE Wiring *Regulations*.

A B C D E F G H I J K L M N O P Q R S T U V W X Y Z

BS 88 high breaking capacity (HBC) fuse

A fuse used when an abnormally high prospective short-circuit current exists, for example to protect motor circuits and industrial installations. The fuse has a silica-filled porcelain body, a silver element, lug-type end caps and an indicating bead to show when the fuse element has blown.

Disadvantages of BS 88 fuses	Advantages of BS 88 fuses
They are very expensive to replace Stocks of these spares are costly and take up space Care must be taken when replacing them, to ensure that the replacement fuse has the same rating and also the same characteristics as the fuse being replaced	They have no mechanical moving parts The element does not weaken with age Operation is very rapid under fault conditions It is difficult to interchange the cartridge, since different ratings are made to different physical sizes

▲ Advantages and disadvantages of BS 88 fuses

BS 1361/BS 1362 cartridge fuses

A porcelain tube filled with granulated silica and with the element attached to the metal end caps:

- BS 1361 is used in distribution boards and at main intake positions.
- BS 1362 is used in domestic plugs in conjunction with 13 A BS 1363 domestic socket outlets.
- BS 1362, fuse rating 3 amps, is used with appliances up to 720 watts.
- BS 1362, fuse rating 13 amps, is used with appliances up to 3000 watts.
- BS1362 is also available in fuse ratings 1, 5, 7 and 10 amps.

▲ BS 1361 and BS 1362 fuses

A
B
C
D
E
F
G
H
I
J
K
L
M
N
O
P
Q
R
S
T
U
V
W
X
Y
Z

BS 3036 fuse

An older rewirable *fuse* incorporating a fuse element, a bakelite or porcelain holder and carrier, and possibly an asbestos pad to quench any arc drawn during fuse element rupture. The fuse holder is colour coded to show the appropriate circuits for the type of fuse: white for 5 A; blue for 15 A; yellow for 20 A; red for 30 A; green for 45 A. BS 3036 fuses are cheap to manufacture but are unreliable as they can be rewired with the wrong rating of fuse wire and have a poor fusing factor.

▲ BS 3036 rewirable fuse

busbar trunking

This is wide, flat trunking with three or four busbars fixed onto moulded block insulators, used to distribute *three-phase power* in commercial and industrial applications. The conductors are usually copper and may have an insulating sleeve. The copper may be round, oval or rectangular and will vary in thickness according to the current to be carried. Busbar trunking is available in right-angle bends, tee pieces and crossovers, and in ratings up to many hundreds of amps. Connection is made onto the busbar trunking via fused tap-off boxes which reduce the fuse rating down from the busbar rating to one suitable for the final circuit and its associated equipment.

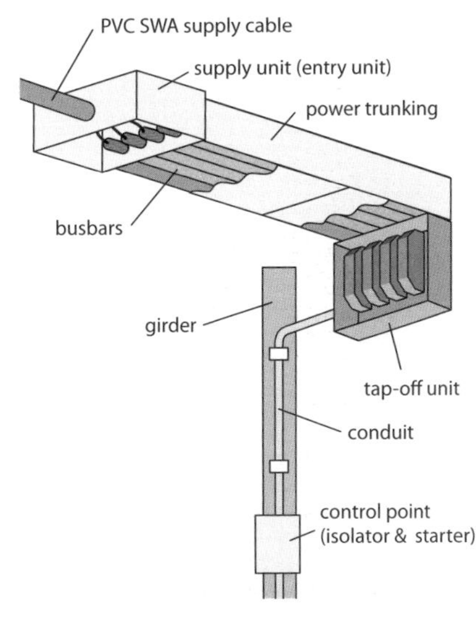

▲ Power trunking showing tap-off unit

busbar trunking (rising mains)
Purpose-made busbar trunking which runs vertically through the walls of multi-storey buildings with a fixed fuse-box on each floor.

cable

A conductor used to carry current around an installation. Cables are identified by the colour of the insulation; see the table below.

Function	Colour
Protective conductors	Green and yellow
Functional earthing conductor	Cream
a.c. power circuit[1]	
Phase of single-phase circuit	Brown
Neutral of single- or three-phase circuit	Blue
Phase 1 of three-phase a.c. circuit	Brown
Phase 2 of three-phase a.c. circuit	Black
Phase 3 of three-phase a.c. circuit	Grey
Two-wire unearthed d.c. power circuit	
Positive of two-wire circuit	Brown
Negative of two-wire circuit	Grey
Two-wire earthed d.c. power circuit	
Positive (of negative earthed) circuit	Brown
Negative (of negative earthed) circuit	Blue
Positive (of positive earthed) circuit	Blue
Negative (of positive earthed) circuit	Grey

▲ Identifying cable insulation in accordance with BS 7671 colours *(continued)*

A B C D E F G H I J K L M N O P Q R S T U V W X Y Z

Function	Colour
Three-wire d.c. power circuit Outer positive of two-wire circuit derived from three-wire system Outer negative of two-wire circuit derived from three-wire system Positive of three-wire circuit Mid-wire of three-wire circuit[2] Negative of three-wire circuit	 Brown Grey Brown Blue Grey
Control circuits, ELV and other applications Phase conductor	Brown, black, red, orange, yellow, violet, grey, white, pink or turquoise
Neutral or mid-wire[3]	Blue

NOTES
(1) Power circuits include lighting circuits.
(2) Only the middle wire of three-wire circuits may be earthed.
(3) An earthed PELV conductor is blue.

▲ Identifying cable insulation in accordance with BS 7671 colours

Conductor	Old colour
Phase	Red
Neutral	Black
Protective conductor	Green and yellow
Phase one	Red
Phase two	Yellow
Phase three	Blue
Neutral	Black
Protective conductor	Green and yellow

▲ Old conductor insulation colours

Installations connected prior to 1 April 2004 will have cables coded with the old insulation colours.

See *MICC cable (mineral-insulated copper cable)*; *Single core PVC insulated unsheathed cable*; *Single core PVC insulated sheathed cable*

cable basket

A steel wire basket used to support cable. Bolt cutters are used to cut the basket to form bends or tees, which are then smoothed.

cable ladder

A cable support for transporting cables across long spans. It is made in various widths and prefabricated sections, components and accessories, making it easy to assemble. It is also very sturdy and can withstand very adverse conditions.

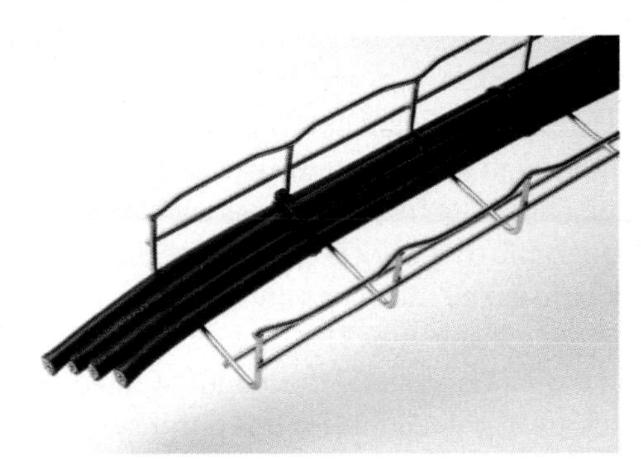

▲ Cable basket

▲ Cable ladder

cable routes (cable run)

The route that cables take in an installation, which ensures that they are in a safe position and protected from mechanical damage, such as corrosion or exposure to sharp edges or contact with other services such as gas or water. The IEE On-Site Guide gives details regarding permitted cable routes. If these routes are not possible, the cable should be installed in earthed metal *conduit* or *trunking*.

cable run

See *Cable routes*

cable selection

The correct cable for a particular installation is selected according to certain factors. These factors include:

- the environment of the installation (e.g. *ambient temperature*)
- the design *current*
- the rating of the *protective device*
- correction factors (e.g. ambient temperature, *grouping factors*, *thermal insulation*, *BS 3036 fuse* and *cable* correction factors)
- shock protection
- thermal constraints
- current carrying capacity and voltage drop.

cable tray

A perforated metal tray on to which cables can be clipped or tied. Cable trays are normally concealed in the ceiling making it difficult to cause damage to the cables.

A B C D E F G H I J K L M N O P Q R S T U V W X Y Z

Cable trays may be used on large industrial and commercial installations where several cables take the same route. A wide range of designs of cable tray and accessories are available to match any cabling requirement, from lightweight instrumentation cable through to the heaviest multicore power cable. In situations where heavy multicore cables are required to cross long, unsupported spans, *cable ladders* should be used.

Cable tray bends can be formed by hand after a number of cuts have been made in the flange to accommodate the bend, although a far better job can be made by using a crimping tool or a tray-bending machine. Bending machines are available from various manufacturers. Where a lot of cable tray work is to be installed, machine bending is quicker and more practical. The machines are made to accommodate the various widths and gauges of cable tray. They may also be used to bend and form flat strips of metal, and have a vice to hold the length of cable tray being worked upon. Cable tray chain vices are also available for this purpose.

calibration of instruments

Checking the accurate setting of instruments used for taking measurements. Electrical test instruments must be calibrated in specialist test laboratory conditions against national standards at least every 12 months, and always after an accident or damage. Tested instruments are given a calibration label with the date of the last calibration and the date when the instrument should be tested again. A calibration certificate is also issued giving details of the tests performed.

cameras

See *CCD camera*; *Closed-circuit television (CCTV)*; *CMOS camera*

capacitance

The ability to store electric *charge*. Capacitance (C) is measured in microfarads (μF), nanofarads (nF) or picofarads (pF).

See *Capacitor*

capacitive circuit

These include either *capacitors* or long runs of circuit wiring producing a capacitive effect, for example long runs of mineral-insulated cable or long runs of underground cable. After turning off the power, the stored electric *charge* must be completely discharged before starting any electrical work.

capacitive reactance

In a *capacitive circuit*, the opposition to a.c. current is called capacitive reactance (X_C), measured in ohms (Ω). In this case, the current leads the voltage by 90° and can be calculated by using the following formula:

$$X_C = \frac{1}{2\pi fC}$$

Where:

f = supply frequency (hertz – Hz)
C = circuit capacitance (farads – F)

capacitor

A component which stores an electric *charge* when a *potential difference* is applied across it, and which returns the charge to the circuit. The two main categories of capacitor are: fixed (electrolytic and non-electrolytic) and variable. A capacitor connected to an *a.c.* supply stores and discharges electrical charge as the current moves through positive and negative cycles. The structure of a capacitor consists of two metallic plates, separated by an insulator, called the *dielectric*. Capacitor symbols are shown in the diagram.

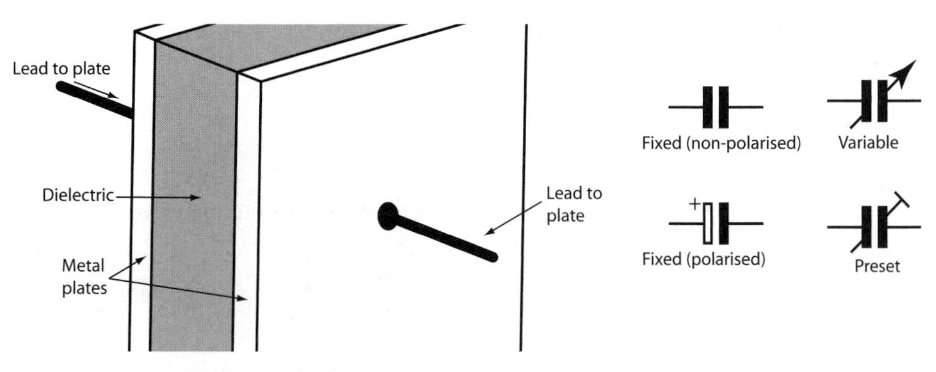

▲ Basic construction of a capacitor, and circuit symbols

The level of *capacitance* depends on the area of the plates, the type of material used and the thickness of the dielectric. Capacitors are coded to show:

- the level of capacitance – in microfarads (μF), nanofarads (nF) or picofarads (pF)
- working voltage (the maximum that the dielectric can handle)
- type of construction
- polarity (if any).

capacitor smoothing

A capacitor may be used to smooth the circuit waveform for small output *currents*. Most circuits have an output current which is slightly, but constantly, changing. For electronic circuits a smooth supply *voltage* is required and the waveform must be 'ripple-free'.

capacitor start/capacitor run motor

An efficient single-phase *induction motor*, combining *capacitor* start and permanent split capacitor design. This motor is used for air compressors and high-pressure water pumps and can handle the most demanding applications for single-phase motors. The start capacitor is in series with the auxiliary winding, providing high starting *torque*; the run capacitor remains in series with the auxiliary winding when the start capacitor switches out.

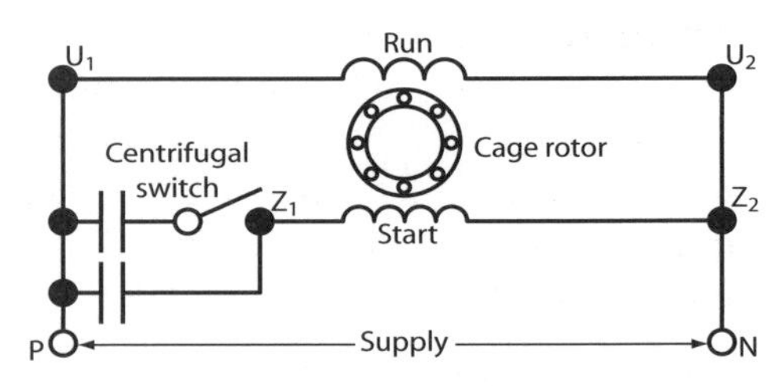

▲ Capacitor start capacitor run split-phase motor

capacitor start/induction run motor

A *capacitor* is connected in series with the start winding, giving a phase difference of nearly 90° between the two *currents* in the windings thus improving the starting performance. This type of motor can have a starting *torque* of 300 per cent of full-load torque, and a starting current up to nine times the full-load current. It is used to drive compressors and small conveyor systems.

▲ Capacitor start motor

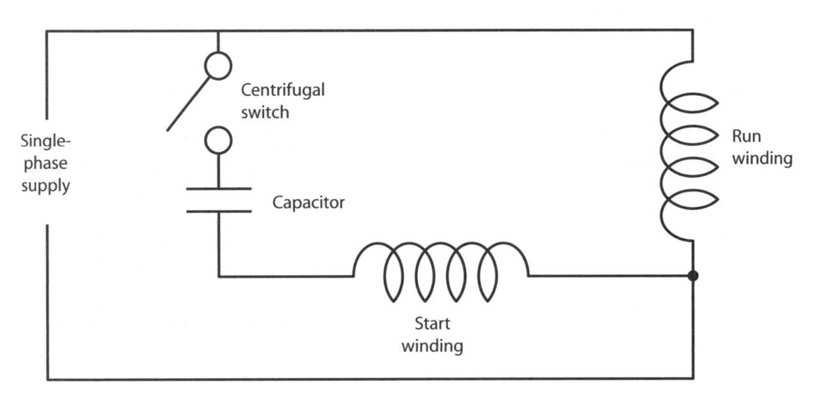

▲ Winding connections for capacitor start split-phase motor

A B C D E F G H I J K L M N O P Q R S T U V W X Y Z

caravan installations

The electricity facilities, at a caravan site, to which caravans are connected for the supply of electricity. Regulations require that a notice is fixed near the main electrical switch of a caravan giving instructions on the connection and disconnection to site electricity supplies. The installation must not be TN-C-S (PME) earthed.

See *Caravan Park Regulations*

Caravan Park Regulations

These are regulations that cover the safe use of electricity supply at caravan parks (e.g. BS Special Location Regulation, Part 6, Section 608 refers to caravan parks). They must be followed to avoid the risk of harm from electric shock, including:

- open circuit faults of the *PEN* conductor in *TN-C-S protective multiple earthing (PME)* supplies
- loss of earthing because of long cable runs
- devices exposed to weather
- flexible cord connections.

The supply at a caravan park should not exceed 250 V/440 V and should be connected by underground cables, and each pitch should have supply equipment within 20 metres. The socket outlet and enclosure must comply with BS EN 60309-2 and Protection IPX4.

carbon brush motor

A motor drawing less than a kilowatt, used to drive drills, vacuum cleaners and washing machines. The power is connected to the *armature* through a system of spring-loaded carbon brushes and a *commutator*.

cartridge fuses

See *BS 1361/BS 1362 cartridge fuses*

castle nut

A nut with a grooved stud. After tightening, a hole is drilled opposite a groove, and a split pin is inserted and splayed to prevent the nut from turning.

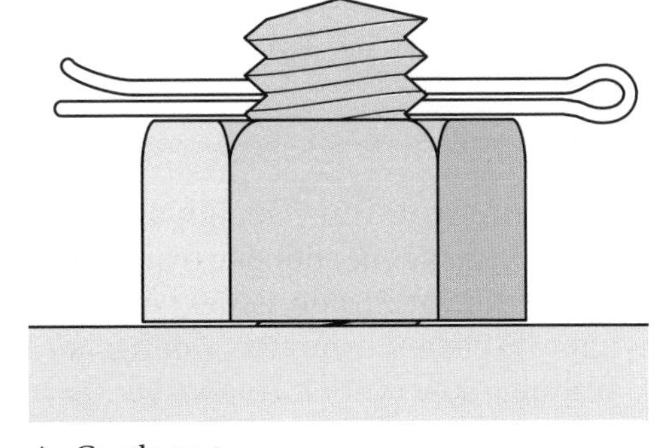

▲ Castle nut

cat 5 cable

A data transfer cable with four unshielded twisted pair (UTP) wires that transmit data at up to 100 Mbps.

cat 5e cable/cat 6 cable

Enhanced versions of *cat 5 cable* made to more stringent standards and designed for speeds of up to 1 Gbps.

A
B
C
D
E
F
G
H
I
J
K
L
M
N
O
P
Q
R
S
T
U
V
W
X
Y
Z

catenary wire

A galvanised steel support wire, erected and tightened between buildings for suspending electrical cables across spans. Cables are attached with tape or suspended on hide hangers. A drip loop of cable should be formed at each end of the span to remove rainwater from the wire.

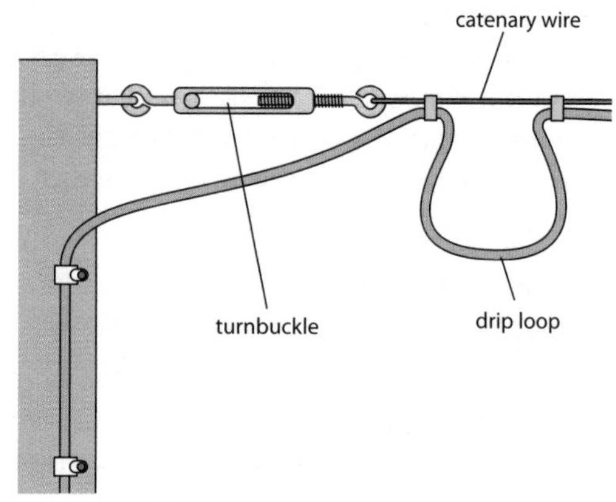

▲ Cable suspension using catenary wire

cathode

A negatively charged electrode. In a low-pressure mercury vapour lamp (*fluorescent lamp*), the cathodes are oxide-coated tungsten filaments, sealed at each end of the tube. The current heats the cathodes forming a cloud of electrons, and these ionise the gas in the tube.

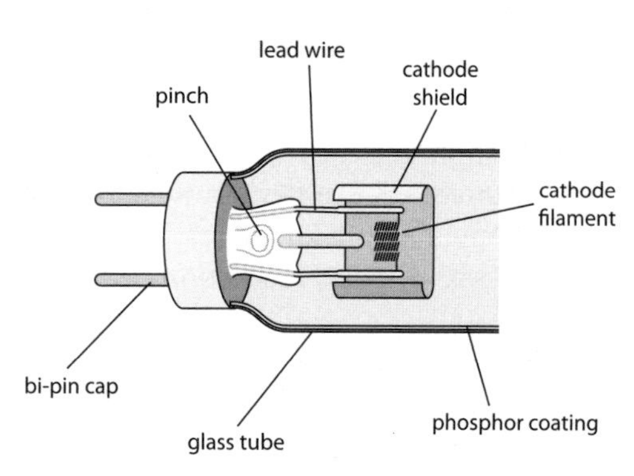

▲ Detail of one end of a fluorescent tube showing a cathode

cathode shield

In large low-pressure mercury vapour lamps, the cathodes have a shield made from iron strips bent to enclose the cathode and trap the material given off. This reduces the blackening at the tube ends.

CCD camera

A CCTV camera which uses a charged coupled device (CCD), in the form of a piece of silicon, instead of a film, and produces very sharp images.

CCTV

See *Closed-circuit television*

CDM/Construction (Design and Management) Regulations (1994)

These Regulations stipulate requirements for cooperation on duties involved with Health and Safety issues on large construction projects. The Regulations apply to clients, contractors, designers and the planning supervisor. The planning supervisor is responsible for producing a Health and Safety plan and for the co-ordination and management of Health and Safety at the beginning of the project. A principal contractor is appointed to co-ordinate and manage health and safety issues during construction work and for keeping the Health and Safety file up to date.

ceiling rose

A circular fitting on a ceiling from which an electrical light hangs. A pendant ceiling rose lamp holder is connected with a flexible cable or cord which must comply with the appropriate British and Harmonised European standards (refer to *IEE Wiring Regulations* 521-01-01).

CENELEC

This is the European Committee for Electrotechnical Standardisation that oversees the harmonisation of standards of electrical and electronic goods and services throughout the European Union.

centrifugal switch

A device used to disconnect the start windings on a single-phase split-phase *induction motor* when the motor is approaching full speed. It relies on the rotation of the shaft to move two spring-loaded weights which open a set of contacts. Failure to disconnect the start winding would result in its premature failure. The operation of the centrifugal switch can often be heard as a distinct 'click'.

certification

There are three types of electrical certificate required to approve the installation/alteration of electrical appliances:

- *Electrical Installation Certificate* (for new installations or major alterations)
- *Minor Works Certificate* (for small projects, such as adding a socket outlet or lighting point to an existing circuit)
- *Periodic Inspection and Test Certificate* (for periodic inspections and tests on existing installations).

These certificates include an *Inspection Schedule* and a Test Results Schedule.

charge

A quantity of electricity measured in *coulombs* and designated by the symbol Q.

chasing

This is creating channels in a wall for *conduit* or cable runs, so that the finished work is level with the wall. The channel may be created using a bolster chisel and hammer, a chasing tool or a special attachment on an electric drill.

choke

A coil of low *resistance* and high *inductance* used to pass direct current but attenuate alternating current. For example, in a *fluorescent lamp* a choke may be used to increase the voltage to the level required for *ionisation* of the gas. The choke also acts as a current-limiting device as the *impedance* limits the current through the lamp.

choke inductance

See *Ballast inductance*

A B C D E F G H I J K L M N O P Q R S T U V W X Y Z

A B C D E F G H I J K L M N O P Q R S T U V W X Y Z

choke smoothing

If a choke is connected in series with a load, the changing *current* introduces an *electromotive force* in opposition in order to maintain a steady current. The greater the rate of change of the current the more smoothing produced. The choke is more effective than a capacitor for smoothing circuits with a heavy current.

circuit (battery driven)

In a simple battery-driven circuit, the battery produces an *e.m.f.* from an internal chemical reaction, which causes electrons to flow along the conducting wire to the lamp and through the filament in the lamp. The filament heats and glows, producing light. The electrons leave the lamp along the second conductor and return to the battery. If the flow of electrons is interrupted, for example by removing one of the conductors, the light will go out.

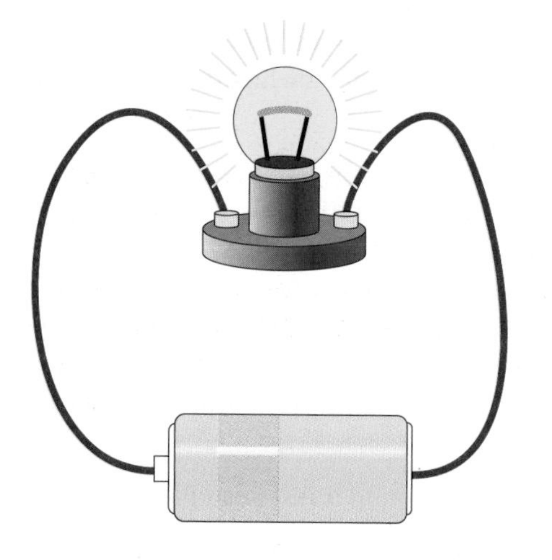

◀ A simple circuit

circuit board

This is an insulated board on which an electric circuit is laid out on an insulated track on to which components are attached by soldering them to the board or by using wires or wire pins. Electronic and solid-state devices use millivolts and milliamperes, and are very sensitive to mains *voltage* and heat. When conducting electrical tests, disconnect any electronic circuit boards before starting as the test voltages could damage the equipment and an inaccurate reading may result.

circuit breaker

A device used for *overcurrent protection* and designed to operate within specified limits. The circuit breaker will disconnect the supply in the event of an overload, short circuit or earth fault. *Miniature circuit breakers (MCBs)* have the break capacity marked as an 'M' number; M6 denotes a breaking capacity of 6000A.

circuit diagram

A simplified diagram showing how the components of a circuit are connected in sequence, using electrical symbols. The diagram is not to scale and does not represent the locations of the components, only the sequence of connections.

See *Layout diagram symbols*

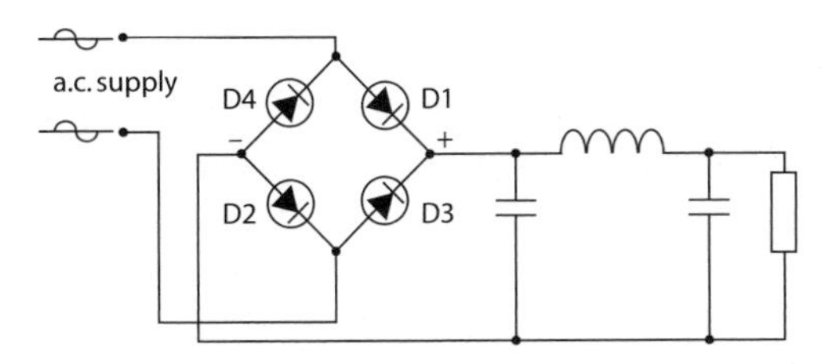

▲ A circuit diagram

circuit protective conductor (cpc)

A system in which conductors are joined together and connected to the main earth terminal. The size of the cpc or earth conductor must comply with the IEE Wiring Regulations and be capable of carrying a *fault current* of hundreds or thousands of amperes. The adiabatic equation is used to work out whether the cpc will carry the fault current without causing heat or fire damage. Refer to Regulation 543-01-01, which requires that 'the cross-sectional area of every protective conductor shall be calculated in accordance with Regulation 543-01-03 (adiabatic equation) or selected in accordance with Regulation 543-01-04 (Table 54G)'.

See *Adiabatic equation*; *Regulations*

cistern-type water heater

A water heater operated at greater than 9 kilowatts and capable of supplying large volumes of hot water to several outlets at the same time.

closed-circuit television (CCTV)

A system in which television cameras are directly linked to receiving monitors, at a separate location, for the purpose of security surveillance, as in the case of banks, shopping centres and streets. There are several types of CCTV system:

- wireless CCTV – no cabling is required as the cameras have an in-built transmitter which sends the image to the monitoring screens or recorders
- wired CCTV – this has cabling connecting the cameras to the monitoring screens or recorder over distances of hundreds of metres
- PC-based systems – a digital system produced by adding a video capture card and surveillance software to a PC. The image is recorded on the hard drive and can be transmitted via the internet to distant locations
- motion detectors – CCTV systems which are activated by motion using *passive infrared sensors (PIRs)*.

A
B
C
D
E
F
G
H
I
J
K
L
M
N
O
P
Q
R
S
T
U
V
W
X
Y
Z

Most CCTV systems have cameras in several different locations, which relay images to a central control and can be viewed or recorded using:

- a video switcher – a device that switches between different camera images one at a time
- a quad processor – a device which shows four camera images on screen simultaneously; either one image or all four may be recorded; quality is poorer when recording four
- a multiplexer – a device which records multiple full-sized images onto one VCR simultaneously; it can also display more than one camera image at a time without losing picture quality.

See *CCD camera*; *CMOS camera*

coefficient of linear expansion

The amount that a material expands when heated, usually expressed as a decimal. It is used to calculate expansion or contraction for a given length of material.

coercivity

The reverse magnetic field required to reduce *flux density* to zero.

See *Hysteresis*; *Remanence*

collector column

A device designed to supply electrical current to a rotating unit, for example slewing cranes and rotating displays. A collector column has the main body in a mounting frame, and an aluminium slip-ring cover with a location pocket for the drive or anchor pin. The slip-ring assembly includes phosphor-bronze slip-rings and dual-leg brush gear with copper graphite brushes, mounted on a mild steel shaft which rotates in self-lubricating bearings.

▲ Collector column

commissioning

This involves demonstrating at the completion of an installation or construction that it operates as it is configured to. It ensures the safe energising and operation of all aspects of an installation. It involves:

- inspecting for compliance with BS 7671, project specification, manufacturers' recommendations and other relevant standards
- conducting pre-commissioning tests, including those such as *continuity*, *polarity* and *insulation resistance*
- advising all concerned parties and then energising the circuits within the installation
- measuring *earth-fault loop impedance* and testing the function of *residual current devices*
- commissioning individual items of equipment, which includes checking the settings of overload devices, *thermostats* and time controllers, then checking the energised operation of the equipment.

commutator

A copper device designed to connect a rotating current-carrying coil to a d.c. supply, for example in a *d.c. motor* or *generator*. This enables the current in the *armature* to be reversed every half rotation. The diagram of the commutator, as shown below, is simplified and shows only two segments, separated by insulation and connected to either side of the loop. Large motors have more than 50 segments, separated by insulation, and hundreds of loops. The coils contact the commutator via carbon brushes which are spring loaded to press against the commutator as it rotates.

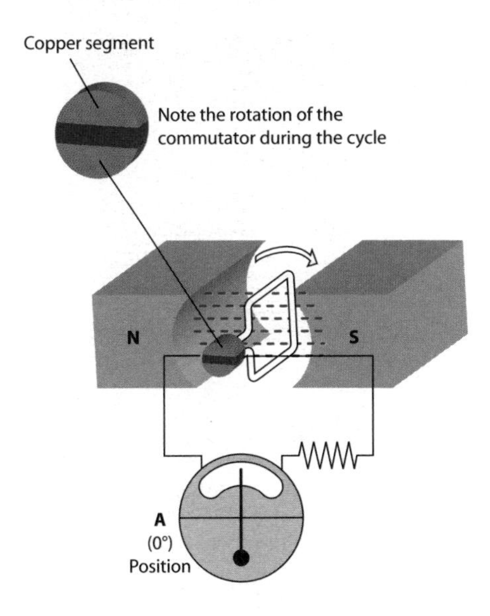

▲ A commutator connected to a generator

A
B
C
D
E
F
G
H
I
J
K
L
M
N
O
P
Q
R
S
T
U
V
W
X
Y
Z

Complementary metal-oxide semiconductor CMOS camera

The complementary metal-oxide semiconductor (CMOS) camera is an inexpensive camera used for CCTV systems. The images are not as clear as those produced by *CCD cameras*.

See *Closed-circuit television (CCTV)*

completion order

A document which is used to record the complete and correct delivery of items listed on a purchase order.

component failure

This occurs when there are faults in electrical circuits, often as a result of everyday wear and tear, but occasionally due to incorrect wiring or inadequate protection. Component failure problems include failure of switches, lamps in lighting circuits, lamps or starters in fluorescent lights.

component positional reference

A grid reference used on electronic circuit board diagrams to identify the location of components on the board. The grid lines may be identified by numbers from the left across the top and by letters down the side, similar to grids used in maps and street directories. The location of components is given by the positional reference, for example 7C or 12N.

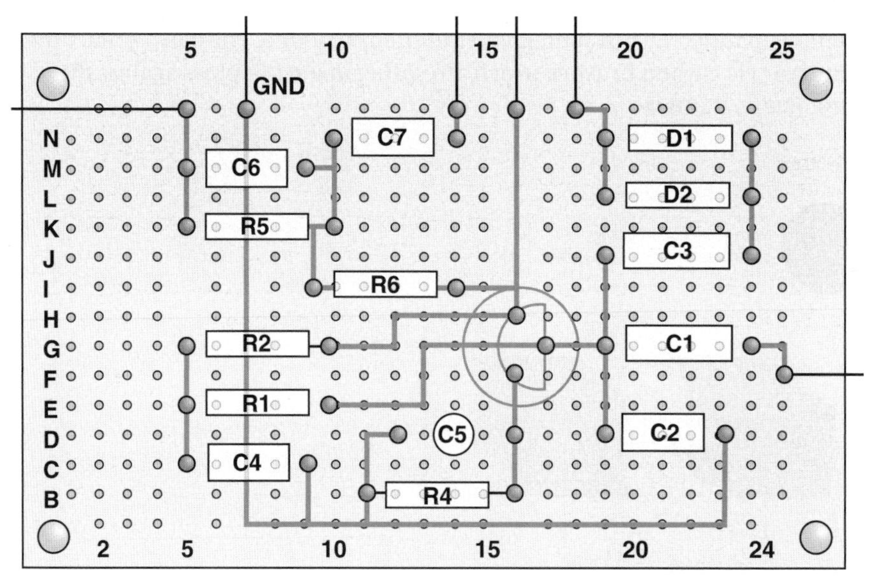

▲ The position of components on an electronic circuit board diagram

compound motor

A type of *d.c. motor*, combining the features of the *shunt* and *series motors*, usually used for bi-directional applications. The compound motor has a high starting *torque* and good speed torque but the controls are complex.

compression joint

A joint formed where connectors are fastened on to conductors with a crimping tool. It is important to ensure that the connection is completely clean before compressing the joint. Any dust caught in the joint could produce increased resistance causing a build-up of heat and a fire risk.

computer disconnection

If the supply to computer equipment is to be disconnected for any reason, for example testing where high voltages may damage the equipment, then it is important to notify all users of the equipment in good time, so that data can be backed up and stored if necessary. If the organisation has an *uninterruptible power supply (UPS)*, the circuits to the computer equipment will remain live when the power is disconnected.

computer installations

The installation of large computer networks using a variety of cables, some of which can carry a combination of voice, data, video and control signals for building services on the one cable. The types of cables used include *Cat 5*, *Cat 5e*, *Cat 6* and *fibre optic*.

conductor

A material that allows the free flow of electrons, which includes the conductors of an electrical circuit, but also refers to metal pipework, metal structures of buildings, salt water or ionised gases which will also allow the transfer of electrical charge. Conductors used for electrical circuits may be stranded (individual strands brought together in set numbers – 3, 7, 19, 37) or solid (easier and cheaper to manufacture but not very pliable). The most commonly used conductors, and the usual applications, are given in the table. Cables with a cross-sectional area (csa) less than 16 mm^2 must have copper conductors. Conductors must be covered with insulating material and protected or placed out of reach 'as far as is reasonably practicable' – refer to Part 2 of BS 7671. The neutral conductor must never have a fuse or switch unless the switch is interlocked to break the phase conductor(s) at the same time.

See *Insulator*; *Ionisation*; *Regulations*; *Semiconductor*

A B C D E F G H I J K L M N O P Q R S T U V W X Y Z

Aluminium (Al)	Low cost and weight Not very flexible Used for large power cables
Brass (alloy of Copper and Zinc)	Easily machined Corrosion resistant Used for terminals and plug pins
Carbon (C)	Hard Low friction in contact with other materials Used for machine brushes
Copper (Cu)	Good conductor Soft and ductile Used in most cables and busbar systems
Iron/Steel (Fe)	Good conductor Corrodes Used for conduit, trunking and equipment enclosure
Lead (Pb)	Flexible Corrosion resistant Used as an earth and as the sheath of a cable
Mercury (Hg)	Liquid at room temperature Quickly vaporises Used for contacts Vapour used for lighting lamps
Sodium (Na)	Quickly vaporises Vapour used in lighting lamps
Tungsten (W)	Extremely ductile Used for filaments in light bulbs

▲ Common conductors

conduit

The tubing for protecting electrical cables, usually made from mild steel or PVC. The number of cables allowed in a conduit is calculated by working out the sum of the cross-sectional areas (csa) of the cables, working out the csa of the conduit and finding out what percentage of the conduit csa would be taken up by the total csa of the cables; this should not exceed 45 per cent.

conduit coupling

A running coupling is used to join two *conduits* which cannot be turned. It has one thread which is the length of a normal half-coupling and another which can accommodate a coupling and a locking ring. When the conduits are butted together, the coupling is moved to rest across both the long thread and the shorter thread and is then tightened and locked.

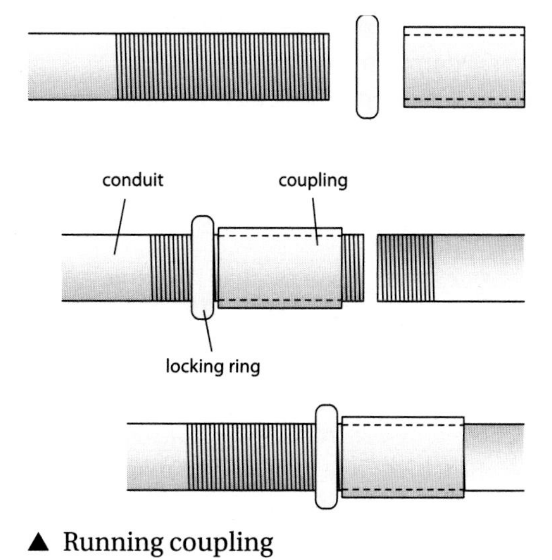

▲ Running coupling

conduit: inspection checklists

When inspecting *conduit* it is important to check that:

- the number of cables does not exceed the maximum
- the number of boxes is sufficient
- solid elbows are confined to permitted use
- the lowest point has drainage holes, as required
- the radius of bends is correct
- the ends of conduit are reamed and bushed
- joints and scratches in metal conduit are protected by paint
- unused entries are sealed.

connector

A joint in non-flexible cables, for coupling two or more cables, which should be soldered, brazed, welded, made using mechanical clamps or with a *compression joint*. The connector should suit the size of the cable and should be insulated according to the *voltage* of the system. If cables with different *insulation* are joined, the insulation of the joint must be the same as the highest level of insulation of the two. Connectors should be chosen to suit the environment and to conform to the appropriate British Standard.

See *Compression joint*; *Junction box; Plastic connector*; *Porcelain connector*; *Screwit*

construction site installations

Installations on a site where work such as new building construction, repair, alteration, extension, demolition, engineering, construction, earthworks or similar, is being carried out. Construction sites have a higher risk of electric shock as the installations are not complete and there is a high level of activity. Therefore these sites are governed by strict *Regulations*. Equipment must be identifiable, colour coded and compatible with the supply. Plugs and sockets must be keyway interlocked. The maximum voltages allowed are:

A B C D E F G H I J K L M N O P Q R S T U V W X Y Z

- safety extra low voltage (SELV) for hand-held lamps in, for example, damp conditions (see *ELV*)
- 110 V, 1 phase, centre-point earthed, for reduced low voltage system, hand-held lamps and tools and local lighting up to 2 kW
- 110 V, 3 phase, star-point earthed, for reduced low voltage system, portable hand-held tools and local lighting up to 2 kW, and small mobile plant to 3.75 kW
- 230 V, 1 phase for floodlighting
- 400 V, 3 phase for fixed and moveable equipment above 3.75 kW.

contactor

A device which uses a *solenoid* effect to make or break contacts. It is found in *motor control circuits, control panels,* electronic controllers and remote switching. In a contactor, a magnetic coil has spring-loaded contacts for auxiliary circuits which are connected or broken when the coil is energised or de-energised. For example, the contactor coils in motor control circuits are energised when the start button is operated. Faults occur when the coils burn out, usually through aging and wear and tear, but this can also occur if the incorrect voltage is used.

See *Remote switching*

contactor starter

A device used in a *direct-on-line (DOL) starter*, providing the simplest method for starting squirrel-cage (induction) motors. The contactor starter connects the full supply voltage directly to the *stator* of the motor.

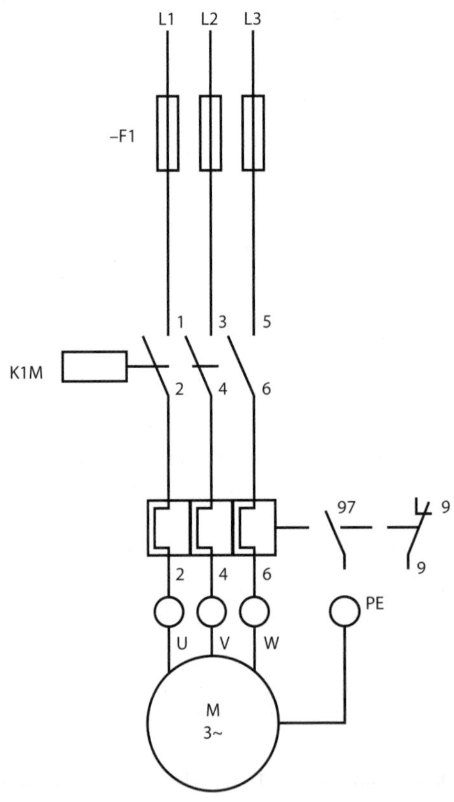

▲ DOL starter showing contactor starter

continuity testing

This is performed periodically using a low-reading *ohmmeter* between all main bonding connections and all supplementary bonding connections. If the installation cannot be isolated, the *protective conductors* must not be disconnected. The main and supplementary bonding conductor readings should be less than 0.05 ohms. If a very high reading is found, then the conductor may be broken or a termination may be disconnected.

contract

A legally binding agreement between two or more parties. If one party does not comply with the terms of the contract, for example fails to commence work on the agreed date, this is a breach of contract and the agreement may be terminated. A fixed-price contract means that the work will be completed for the agreed amount, regardless of actual variations in cost.

control equipment

See *Switchgear*

control panel

The programmable monitor and operator of a system which is connected to all sections of the system. For example, in an alarm system, the control panel operates the alarm sounder when a monitoring device is triggered. Control panels may use a mains supply reduced to an extra low voltage d.c. supply and may also have a backup battery supply, e.g. in a fire alarm panel.

convection heater

Convectors work on the principle of circulating warm air in a room by convection currents. The air warmed by the convection heater becomes lighter and rises to the ceiling. The denser, cold air then replaces it and in turn is heated and rises. Eventually the whole room is heated by this process.

core-type transformer

A transformer with the supply on the primary winding and the output on the secondary winding. The induced *e.m.f.* depends on the number of turns in the primary winding and the number of turns in the secondary winding. Voltage applied to the primary winding produces a changing magnetic flux which circulates in the core and induces an e.m.f. in the secondary winding.

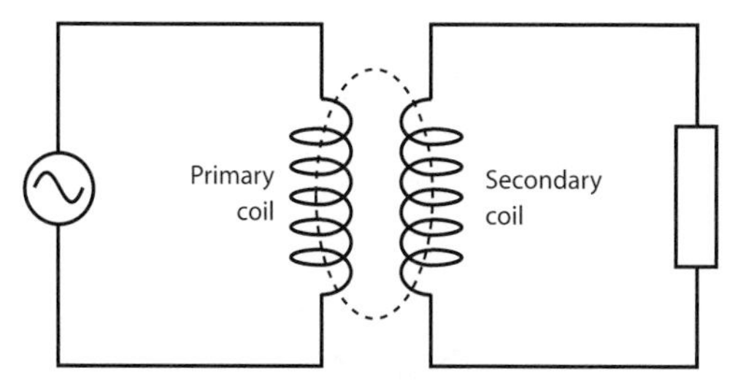

▲ Double wound core-type transformer

A
B
C
D
E
F
G
H
I
J
K
L
M
N
O
P
Q
R
S
T
U
V
W
X
Y
Z

correction factors for cables

There are five correction factors which apply to the selection and installation of cables:

Correction factor	Tables for correction factor values	Symbol
Ambient temperature	Tables 4C1 & 4C2	Ca
Grouping factors	Tables 4B1, 4B2 and 4B3	Cg
Thermal insulation	Regulation 523-04-01	Ci
BS 3036 fuse	0.725 and Table 4C2	Cr
Mineral insulated cable	0.9 Table 4J1A	N/A

▲ Tables for correction factor values

The selection factors ensure that the conductor can carry the current without generating unsafe levels of heat. The correction factors increase the required cross-sectional area of the cable, giving a larger current carrying capacity.

See *Ambient temperature*; *BS 3036 fuse*; *Grouping factors*; *MICC (mineral insulated cable)*; *Thermal insulation*

cosine/cos

The function of an angle in a right-angled triangle. Cos is equal to the ratio of the length of side adjacent to the angle to the length of the *hypotenuse*.

See *Phasor*; *Tangent*

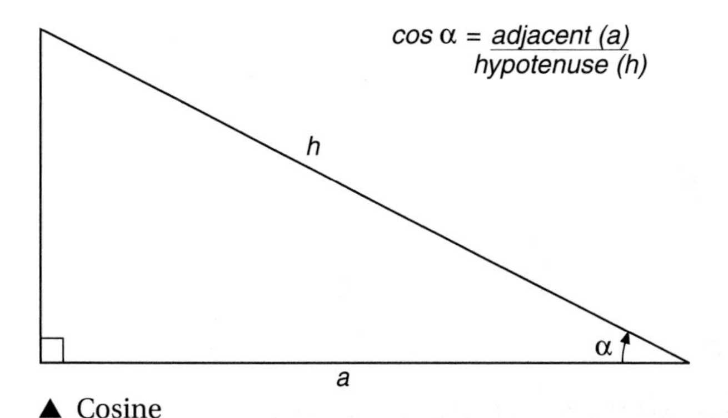

▲ Cosine

coulomb

A unit of electric charge (Q); it is the quantity of electricity transported in one second by a *current* of one ampere.

cpc

See *Circuit protective conductor*

csa

Cross-sectional area; frequently used when describing conductors.

current

The rate of flow of electrical charge in a conductor. Current (I) is measured in amperes (A). The current is driven through the circuit by the e.m.f. (*electromotive force*). The source of e.m.f. could be chemical (e.g. a *battery*), thermal or magnetic.

See *Ohm's Law*

current amplification

See *Transistor*

current, measuring

See *Ammeter*

A
B
C
D
E
F
G
H
I
J
K
L
M
N
O
P
Q
R
S
T
U
V
W
X
Y
Z

current transformer

A transformer used for a.c. current measurement, with a small number of turns on the primary winding and a meter connected across the secondary winding. The secondary winding must never be opened while the primary winding is carrying the main current.

▲ Current transformer

Danfoss Randall Control Packs

These are packs used for control circuits for *timers* and *programmers* with WB12 wiring, which includes terminal-to-terminal wiring details for Heatshare (HSP) and Heatplan (HPP) packs. The supply to the circuit is through a *fused spur* with a 3 A fuse.

data cable

A cable used for transmitting digital information and used for telephones and computers. It comprises twisted pairs of copper conductors or fibre-optic cores through which pulses of laser light can be sent. The cable is very light and fragile, bends should be avoided and specialist tools and equipment are required when installing and terminating these cables.

See *Cable*; *Fibre-optic cable*

d.c.

A direct current, which is an electric current that flows in one direction only. It is produced by, for example, *batteries* for flashlights and portable radios.

See *a.c.*

d.c. generator

A machine where a number of coils are rotated within a *magnetic field*, generating a pulsating *d.c.* via a *commutator*. The *stator* (stationary part) of the generator produces the magnetic field either by permanent magnets or an electromagnetic system.

As a conductor passes through a magnetic field, an e.m.f. is induced in the conductor; the direction of the induced e.m.f. will depend on the direction of movement of the conductor, and the strength of the *e.m.f.* will be determined by the speed at which the conductor moves. If we were to use something to spin a wire loop within a magnetic field, we would then induce into the wire loop an e.m.f., and were we to connect a load to the *armature* via the commutator and brushes, a current would flow around the circuit and the load would work. In other words, we would have created a generator. A variety of sources can be used mechanically to turn the generator's armature, such as steam, wind, waterfall or petrol/diesel engine.

The diagram shows just such an arrangement and the voltage output for one complete revolution. As you can see from the diagram, the output from such a generator has no negative parts in its cycle. This type of generator produces a voltage/current that alternates in magnitude but flows in one direction only; in other words we have a direct current (d.c.). When a d.c. generator contains only a single coil it provides a pulsating d.c. output, as shown by the waveform in the diagram.

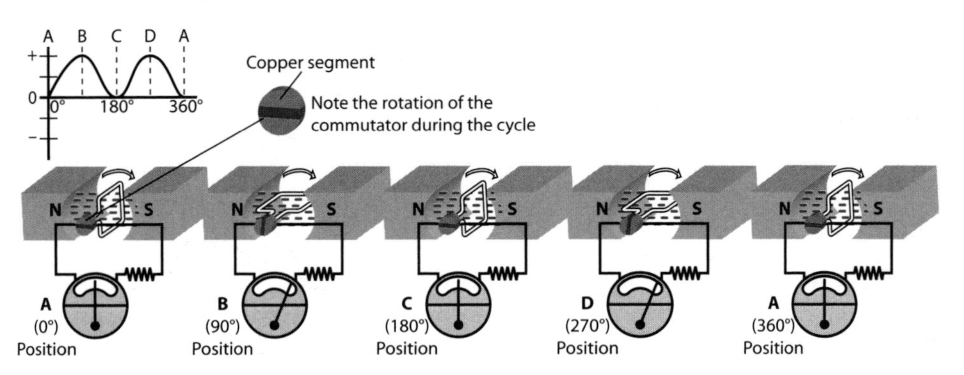

▲ d.c. generator – voltage output for one complete revolution

d.c. motor

A d.c. motor has an electromagnet and a looped conductor, with a central pivot, inside the magnetic field. A direct current is passed through the conductor. A magnetic field is induced around the conductor, which distorts the magnetic field between the poles of the magnet causing the lines of force to stretch. These lines of force attempt to push the conductor out of the magnetic field, causing rotation of the loop. The direction of rotation can be changed by reversing the direction of the magnetic field, or of the current through the armature.

See *Armature*; *Commutator*; *Compound motor*; *Series motor*; *Shunt motor*

d.c. supply

This used to be the main method of transmitting electricity, but a.c. is now preferred as the voltage is easier to adjust, using *transformers*; a.c. motors are also more economic.

See *a.c.*

delta connection

A circuit connection used for a three-phase system with a balanced load where no neutral connection is required, for example power transmission from power stations and three-phase motor windings.

See *Star connection*

▲ Delta connection

detector

See *Voltage detector*; *Voltage-indicating device*

diac

A device used with a *resistor-capacitor* network to produce a pulse-style waveform ideal for *triac*-triggering circuits. The diac provides some protection against unwanted triggers, for example voltage spikes.

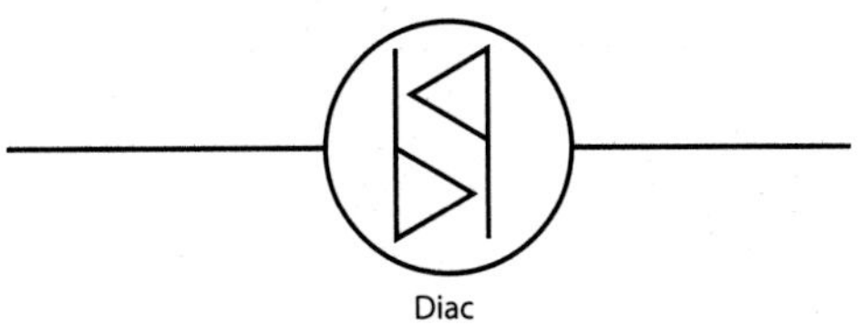

▲ Diac symbol

diagrams

See *Assembly drawing*; *Block diagram*; *Circuit diagram*; *Layout diagram*; *Layout diagram symbols*; *Record (as fitted) drawing*; *Schematic diagram*; *Wiring diagram*

dielectric

Material which is a poor *conductor* of electricity and may be used as an *insulator*, but which also supports an electrostatic field. Dielectrics include vacuums, dry air, mica, glass, porcelain and metal oxides. A dielectric film is used, for example, in a *capacitor*, where charges are displaced but do not flow.

digital device (instrument)

A device used for measurements which shows the information as a numerical display, usually using liquid crystal or *LED* technology, rather than pointing to a measure on a scale.

diode semiconductor

A device that allows current to flow in one direction only.

See *Light-emitting diode (LED)*; *p-n junction*; *Photodiode*; *Semiconductor*; *Solid state equipment*; *Zener diode*

▲ Symbol representing a diode

diode testing

A *p-n junction* diode is in good working order when the *ohmmeter* gives a high *resistance* reading with the positive lead attached to the cathode and the negative lead to the anode and a low resistance reading with the positive lead attached to the anode and the negative lead to the cathode.

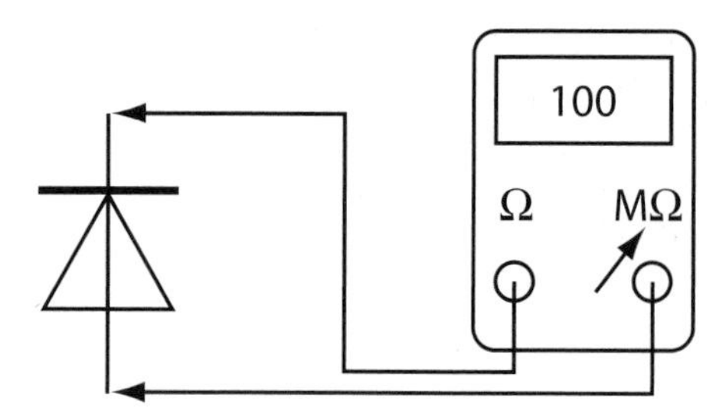

▲ Diode testing – high resistance connection

direct contact protection

Direct contact is contact between a living person or animal and a live part of an electrical installation, such as a *conductor*. Protection from direct contact includes: *insulation*; barriers, such as covers and lids; obstacles, such as fences and barbed wire; installing live parts out of reach; separate extra low voltage (SELV).

See *ELV*

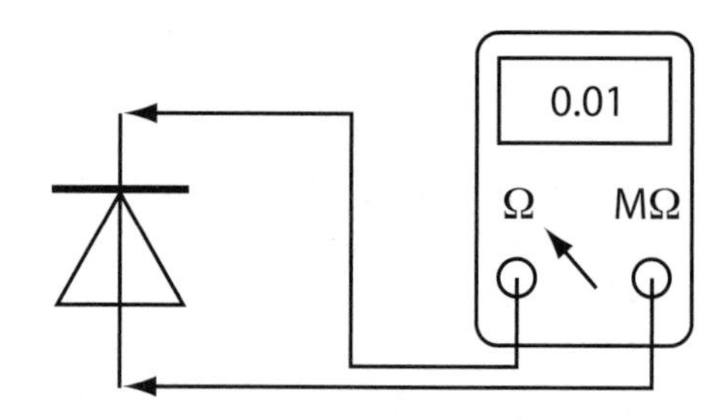

▲ Diode testing – low resistance connection

Direct-on-line (DOL) starter

An economic method used for starting *induction motors*. The full supply *voltage* is directly connected to the *stator* through a contactor starter. A 10 A motor could have a starting *current* up to 60 A, and starting *torque* 150 per cent of the full-load torque. This can cause jumping, therefore DOL starting is most effective on motors up to 5 kW.

▲ DOL starter

directly proportional

The direct relationship between measurements; if one measurement is increased, then the other measurement will also increase. For example, the harder you kick a football, the further it goes.

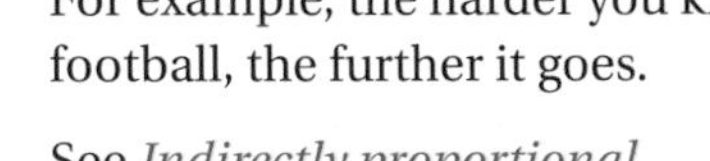

See *Indirectly proportional*

discharge lighting

See *Fluorescent lamp*

discrimination (electrical) – co-ordination of fuses

Discrimination is the correct arrangement of *fuses* and *circuit breakers*. Most installations will have a series of fuses and circuit breakers between the supply and the outlets. Discrimination is the decrease in the rating of the fuses and circuit breakers the closer they are to the current-using equipment. This ensures that the device nearest a fault will operate first.

distribution of electricity

Electricity is distributed to customers from a sub-station to a main intake position at the customer's premises. At the main intake position, the supply company will install a sealed overcurrent device and a metering system to measure usage.

A B C D E F G H I J K L M N O P Q R S T U V W X Y Z

A B C D E F G H I J K L M N O P Q R S T U V W X Y Z

DOL

See *Direct-on-line (DOL) starter*

drawings

See *Diagrams*; *Scaled drawings*

dual-in-line (DIL) integrated circuit

An integrated circuit with the pins lined up on each side, for example an operational amplifier.

See *Integrated circuit*

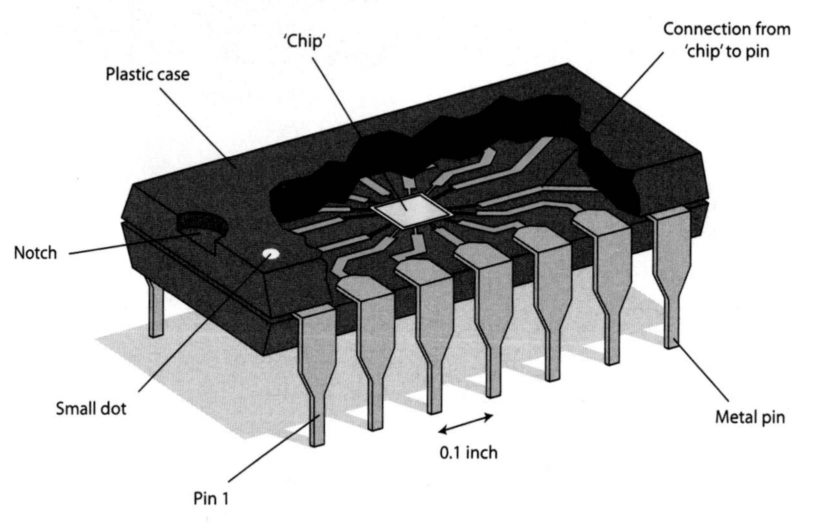

▲ Dual-in-line integrated circuit

earth conductor/earth lead
The conductor which joins an installation's earthing terminal to the earth electrode or electricity supply company's earth terminal. This connection should be labelled 'Safety Electrical Connection – Do not remove'. The cable must be protected against corrosion and should be insulated in green and yellow.

See *Adiabatic equation*; *Protective conductor*

earth electrode
The connection to the actual mass of earth that all earthing arrangements eventually rely upon. The connection to the earth electrode must be made above the ground. An earth electrode may be a special earth rod, pipe, tape, wire or plate, underground metalwork embedded in foundations or a metal pipe. It should, however, never be a gas, oil or water pipe.

earth electrode resistance testing
The resistance of the earth electrode to earth must be measured. This varies according to the type and size of electrode used. The resistance may be measured using an earth electrode resistance tester; switch off the supply and disconnect the earth electrode before testing.

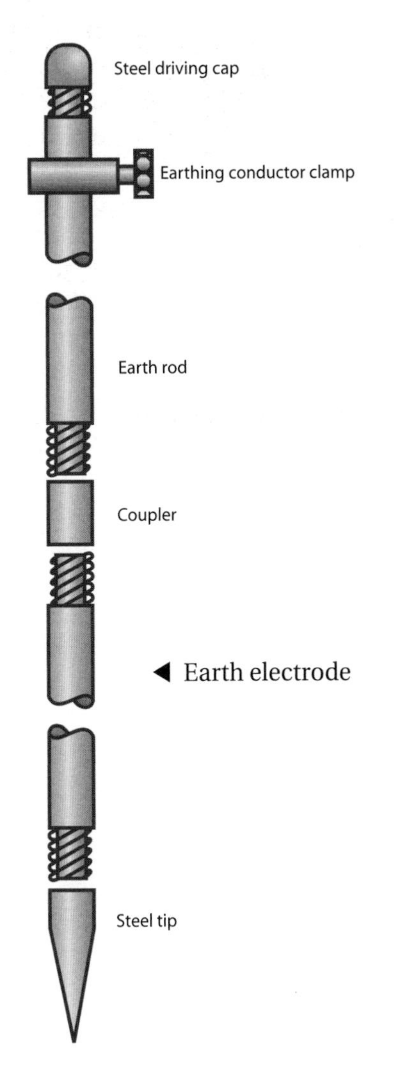

◀ Earth electrode

A B C D E F G H I J K L M N O P Q R S T U V W X Y Z

earth fault

A fault that occurs between any live conductor and earth which causes excessive *current* to flow. Earth faults may be caused by *insulation* breakdown, incorrect polarity, and poor termination of conductors.

Earthed *equipotential bonding* and automatic disconnection of the supply are used to prevent danger from electric shock if there is an earth fault.

See *Protective device*; *Residual current device*

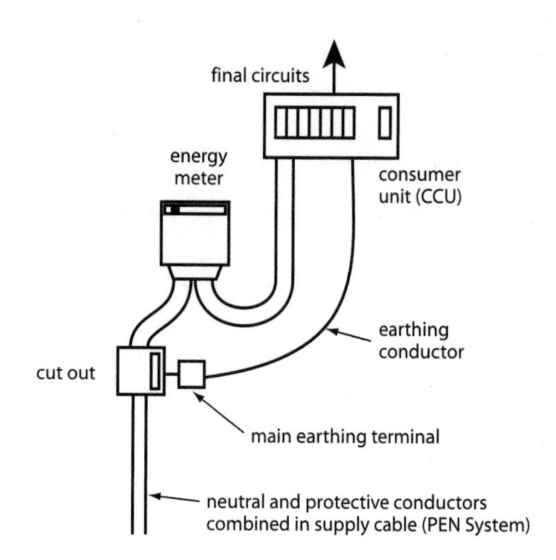

▲ Intake earthing arrangements (in this case TN-C-S)

earth fault loop

The circuit through which the earth *fault current* passes when an earth fault occurs. The earth fault loop has a phase conductor, a *circuit protective conductor*, a main earthing terminal and earth conductor, an earth return path, a path through the earthed neutral of the supply *transformer*, and the secondary winding of the supply transformer.

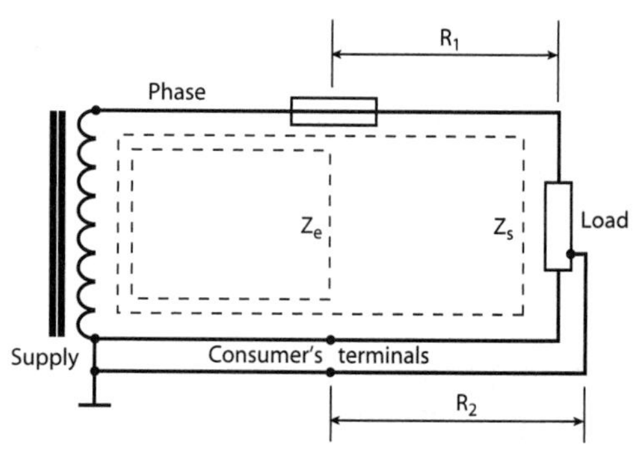

▲ Earth fault loop

earth fault loop impedance

The resistive effect of the *earth fault loop*. The term 'impedance' is used because part of the circuit is inductive, which, when combined with the resistance of the cables to and from the fault, makes up the impedance.

See *Earth conductor*

earth loop impedance tester

This device can measure prospective short-circuit current as well as earth-loop impedance and has *LED* warning lights to indicate correct or incorrect polarity.

▲ Earth loop impedance tester

earthing

This connects metalwork to earth to prevent dangerous *potential differences* between different metals or between metals and earth. Correct earthing procedures prevent danger to life and the risk of fire from excessive currents.

eddy current (Foucault current)

An electric current induced in a *conductor* when the conductor is exposed to a changing magnetic flux. Eddy currents can prove harmful where individual live wires do not pass through the same hole in a ferrous enclosure. This can be remedied by slotting the metal between the holes or using non-ferrous (eg aluminium) gland plates.

EEBADOS (EEBADS)

Earthed equipotential bonding and automatic disconnection of the supply.

efficiency

The ratio of the output to the input of a system, expressed as a percentage.

electric shock

A person may receive an electric shock by touching any live part of a system, causing an electric *current* to pass through the body. A shock may also result from contact with a circuit with too much *resistance*, known as a bad earth circuit. The severity of shock will depend upon the health of the individual, the nature of the surroundings and the type of supply but it is generally accepted that a current above 50 mA can be lethal.

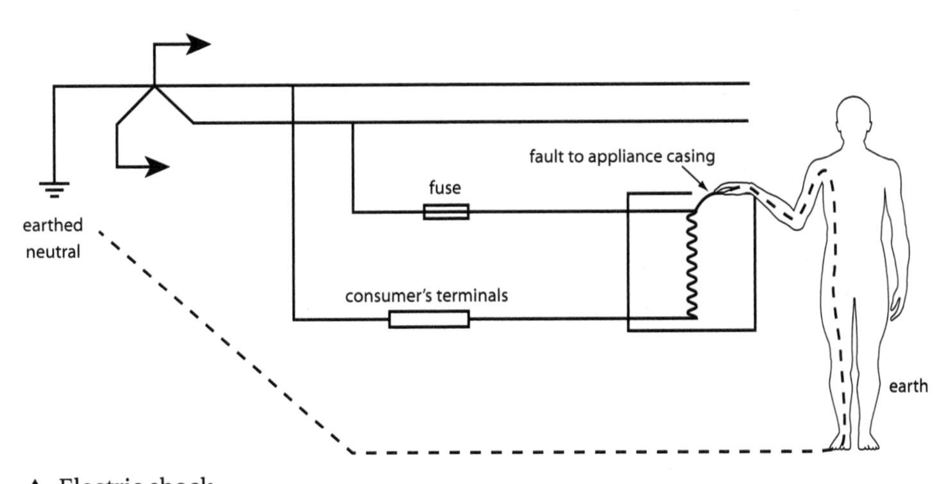

▲ Electric shock

A
B
C
D
E
F
G
H
I
J
K
L
M
N
O
P
Q
R
S
T
U
V
W
X
Y
Z

Electrical Installation Certificate

A document which accompanies the schedule of test results for new or altered installations, confirming that the installation complies with all relevant standards. The certificate should show who was responsible for the design, construction, and inspection and testing. Refer to Appendix 6 of the IEE Wiring *Regulations*, the IEE On-Site Guide and IEE Guidance Notes 3. The Electrical Installation Certificate is given to the person who ordered the work to be done.

electrical symbols

See *Layout diagram symbols*

electricity

See *Distribution of electricity*; *Generation of electricity*; *Transmission of electricity*

Electricity at Work Regulations (EAWR) 1989

The Regulations which impose Health and Safety requirements, related to electricity at work, on employers, self-employed people and employees. Penalties may be imposed on people found guilty of breaching the Regulations. Trainees are considered employees under the Regulations and have a duty to follow the requirements. There are 33 Regulations and 3 Appendices. It is important to know which of these apply to you and your work so that you can ensure that you do not break the law or cause injury, harm or damage.

Electricity Safety, Quality and Continuity Regulations 2002

These regulations replace the Electricity Supply Regulations and require standards of safety to protect the general public from electrical dangers, and standards of quality of power and continuity of supply. The organisations responsible for generating, distributing and supplying electricity, and meter operators and any contractors or agents of these organisations, have duties under these Regulations.

electromagnet

This is a temporary magnet produced when an electric *current* flows through a *conductor*, creating a *magnetic field*. The direction and strength of the field depends on the direction and strength of the current.

electromagnetic force

A magnetic field is created around a *conductor* when an electric *current* passes through it. An electromagnetic force is created when this field interacts with another magnetic field. The electromagnetic force can be used in several ways from *induction motors* to electromagnets used in industry.

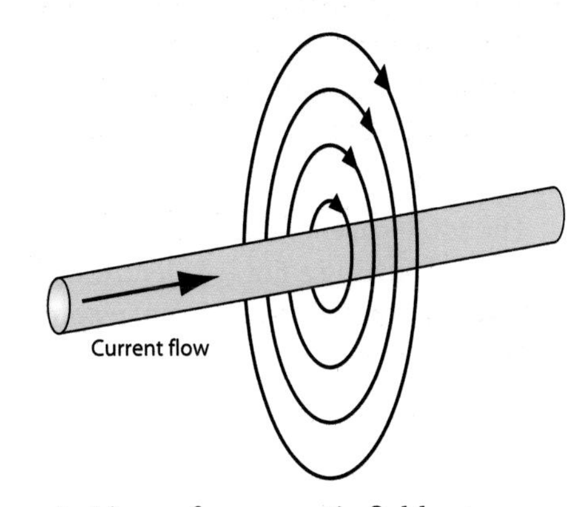

▲ Lines of a magnetic field set up around a conductor

Most motors use the principle that a current-carrying conductor placed in a magnetic field will experience a force. In the first diagram, the direction of the current through the conductor produces a clockwise magnetic field. This distorts the field between the two poles of the magnet producing weakness in the section below the conductor, where the two fields oppose each other, and more strength in the section above, where the two fields have the same direction. The difference in the force on the conductor moves the conductor downwards. If the direction of current through the conductor is changed, or the direction of the field between the magnetic poles is reversed, then the conductor will move upwards.

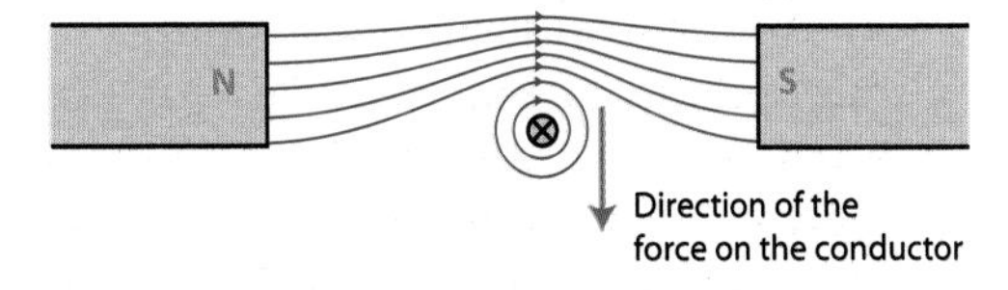

▲ Electromagnetic force – the magnetic field when the conductor is placed between the poles

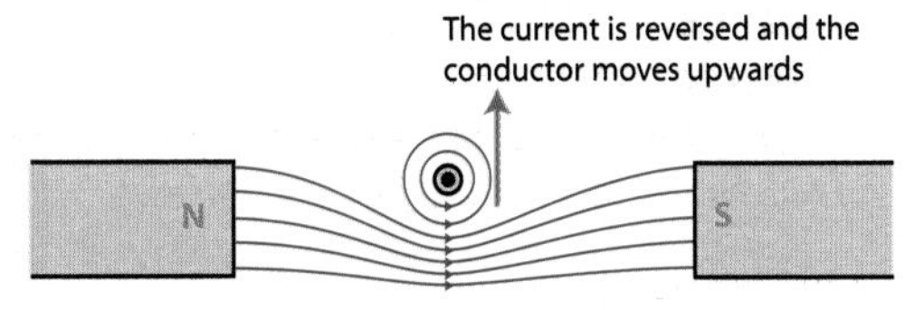

▲ Electromagnetic force – the effect of reversing the direction of the current or magnetic field

A B C D E F G H I J K L M N O P Q R S T U V W X Y Z

electromagnetic induction

The creation of a flow of electric *current* produced when a *conductor* is moved through a *magnetic field*, causing an *electromotive force (e.m.f.)*. In a closed circuit the e.m.f. will cause an electric current.

electromotive force (e.m.f.)

The total force, measured in volts, causing a *potential difference* between two points, causing a flow of electrons. The e.m.f. may be produced by chemical reaction (two different metal electrodes immersed in an electrolyte will result in a flow of electrons), thermal difference (a closed circuit with two different metal junctions at different temperatures produces an e.m.f.), or *electromagnetic induction*.

electronic equipment

Equipment that operates using sensitive voltage and current ranges in millivolts and milliamps and which should be disconnected before testing power circuits.

electronic variable speed drive

A device used to provide precisely controlled variable *voltage* and *frequency* supply for applications such as process automation and variable speed conveyor systems.

electrostatic discharge

A charge produced by a surplus or shortage of electrons on a surface, causing a *potential difference*. An electrostatic discharge may be caused by friction (when two surfaces rub against each other, electrons are transferred – one surface may lose electrons and become positively charged and *vice versa*) and *induction* (a charged item will induce a charge into any other item it comes into contact with – if the item is a non-conductor, the charge remains on the surface).

▲ Static electricity

ELV (extra low voltage)

An ELV circuit is one in which the electrical potential of any conductor against earth is not more than 50 V for alternating current and not more than 120 V for direct current. The use of extra low voltage (ELV) in an electrical circuit is one of several means to provide protection against *electric shock*.

There are three types of extra low voltage sources which are distinguished by their safety properties:

- Separated extra low voltage (SELV) which must be safely separated from other circuits that carry higher voltages; isolated from earth (ground) and from the protective earth conductors of other circuits.
- Protected extra low voltage (PELV) which has a protective earth (ground) connection. A PELV circuit requires a design that guarantees a low risk of accidental contact with a higher voltage.
- Functional extra low voltage (FELV) describes any other extra low voltage circuit that does not fulfil the requirements for an SELV or PELV circuit.

emergency escape lighting

Lighting used for safe exit from public buildings in the event of a power failure. It shows the escape routes, with guidance at each change of level or direction, provides horizontal lighting of at least 0.2 lux along the centre lines of escape routes (escape route lighting) and ensures visibility of fire-alarm call points, fire-fighting equipment and obstructions.

emergency lighting

Lighting used in and around public buildings to illuminate and identify exit routes and provide security. Emergency lighting must conform to *British Standards* requirements (BS 5266 Part 1: 1999 – Code of Practice for Emergency Lighting and EN 1838). Emergency lighting should always have its own separate emergency battery power source or battery backup system so that the lighting will always operate (usually for at least three hours) in the case of power failure. There are three main types of system:

- maintained – lamps are used by both mains and backup systems and operate continuously even if the mains power fails; if the lamp is not illuminated it needs to be replaced
- non-maintained – lamps operate only when the usual lighting system fails; lamps must be checked regularly to ensure that they are operational
- sustained – a lamp in the mains luminaire that is used only when the mains fails.

See *Emergency escape lighting*; *High-risk-task area lighting*; *Open area (anti-panic) lighting*; *Standby lighting*

A B C D E F G H I J K L M N O P Q R S T U V W X Y Z

A B C D E F G H I J K L M N O P Q R S T U V W X Y Z

e.m.f.

See *Electromotive force*

energy

This is the ability to perform work or to move or change things – it cannot be created or destroyed. Energy may be chemical, electrical, thermal, light, mechanical, nuclear, solar, water, wind or many other forms. There are two types: potential (stored energy – increasing or decreasing according to circumstances, e.g. a brick lying on the ground has very little, but a loose brick on top of a wall has quite a lot) and kinetic energy (motion – the more mass a moving object has, and the faster it is travelling, the more kinetic energy it has).

equipotential bonding

The connection and *earthing* of all the metalwork in a building using *conductors* and 'earth clamps', or clips, to prevent the build-up of dangerous voltages in the event of an electrical fault. The metalwork is kept at equal potential so that dangerous potentials cannot exist. Equipotential bonding is a requirement of the electrical wiring *Regulations* BS7671.

equipotential bonding conductors – testing

Testing the continuity of the equipotential bonding conductors. The conductors should be disconnected from the main earthing terminal for the test. If the installation cannot be isolated from the supply, do not disconnect the equipotential bonding conductors; if there is a fault, metalwork could become live.

explosive areas – installations

Hazardous areas where there is a risk of explosion or fire caused by the ignition of gas, dust or flammable liquids. A hazardous area is any area where explosive gas and air mixtures could arise and be present in large enough quantities to warrant special precautions for electrical installations. They are classified into three zones:

- Zone 0 – an explosive gas atmosphere is present continuously or for long periods
- Zone 1 – an explosive gas atmosphere is likely to occur in normal operation
- Zone 2 – an explosive gas atmosphere is not likely to occur and, if it does, will exist for a very short time.

Electrical ignition sources include electrical equipment and lights, sparks from electrical equipment, stray currents from electrical equipment, electrostatic discharge sparks and electromagnetic radiation. Make sure that electrical equipment and instrumentation is classified for the zone in which it is located, and correctly earthed.

Zone 0	Zone 1	Zone 2
Category 1	Category 2	Category 3
'ia' intrinsically safe EN 50020, 2002	'd' flameproof enclosure EN 50018 2000	Electrical Type 'n' EN 50021 1999 Non electrical EN 13463-1, 2001
Ex s – Special protection if specially certified for Zone 0	'p' pressurised EN 50016 2002	
	'q' powder filling EN 50017, 1998	
	'o' oil immersion EN 50017, 1998	
	'e' increased safety EN 50019, 2000 'ib' Intrinsically safe EN 50020, 2002	
	'm' encapsulation EN 50028, 1987	
	's' special protection	

▲ Classification of hazardous areas

IEC Standard BS EN 60079: Part 10 is the classification of hazardous areas, Part 14 specifies electrical apparatus for explosive gas atmospheres and Part 17 specifies the inspection and maintenance required for electrical installations in hazardous areas. The Dangerous Substances and Explosive Atmospheres Regulations (DSEAR) 2002 also apply to hazardous areas and the Petroleum (Regulations) Acts 1928 and 1936, and local licensing laws, cover the storage of petroleum.

exposed conductive parts

The accessible parts of an electrical installation which are safe to touch under normal conditions, but which are capable of conducting electricity under fault conditions, such as the metal casing of a heater or oven, metal conduit, tray plate and *trunking*. Exposed conductive parts must be bonded to earth correctly.

A B C D E F G H I J K L M N O P Q R S T U V W X Y Z

external influence classification

External influences such as temperature, humidity and corrosion are classified according to Appendix 5 of BS 7671. A two-letter, one-number code is designated to all external influences, for example, AD3 means an environmental influence, (A) in the form of water (D) and involving splashes (Level 3).

See *Regulations*

extraneous conductive parts

The metal parts of a building capable of conducting electricity but not part of the electrical installation, for example copper water pipes and boilers. These parts may become live if there is a fault and should be bonded correctly to earth.

Faraday's Law

This states that when a *conductor* cuts a *magnetic field*, or is cut by a magnetic field, then an *e.m.f.* is induced in the conductor. The magnitude of the e.m.f. is proportional to the rate at which the conductor cuts the magnetic flux, or the rate at which the magnetic flux cuts the conductor.

fault

A defective point in an electric circuit due to a crossing of the parts of the *conductor*, or to contact with another conductor or the earth, or to a break in the circuit, or to an *insulation* failure. Normally the *resistance* between live conductors or between live conductors and earth at the fault position is low, thus will cause a *fault current* to flow through an abnormal or unintended path.

fault current

A current caused by a fault in a circuit. The fault current may flow at a level up to and including the prospective *short circuit* current. Faults may be caused by a wiring fault or a screw or drill bit driven through a live conductor.

See *Earth fault*; *Overcurrent*; *Overload current*; *Prospective short circuit current*; *Protective device*

fault detector coil

See *Residual current device*

A B C D E F G H I J K L M N O P Q R S T U V W X Y Z

fault diagnosis

The analysis of problems within a faulty wiring system and the associated investigation. When faults occur an electrician should be able to recognise when an installation and its components are not functioning properly, locate and rectify the fault, and re-commission the equipment or system. Faults may include:

- complete loss of supply
- localised loss of supply
- operation of overload and *fault current* devices
- *transient voltages*
- *insulation* failure
- plant, equipment or component failure
- abuse, misuse or neglect of system or components.

A good procedure for fault diagnosis is to identify and analyse the symptoms, check the supply and *protective devices*, isolate the section, test and interpret

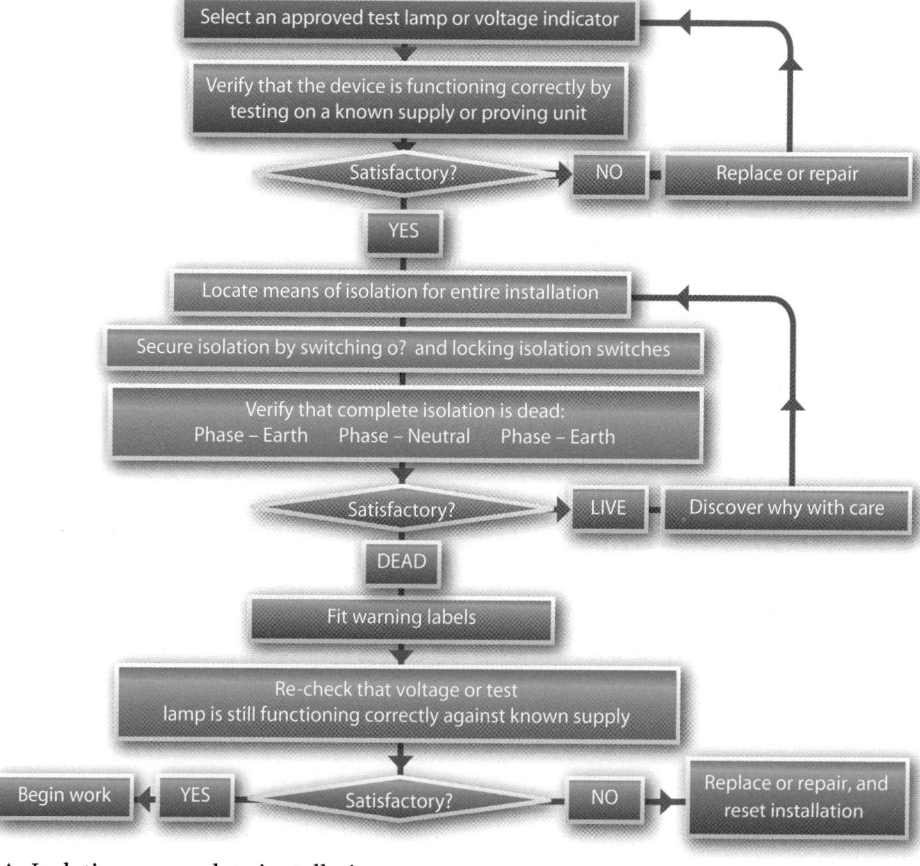

▲ Isolating a complete installation

tests, rectify the fault and test the functionality of the section and the system, then restore the supply. The information required when attending a fault call-out includes:

- the location of incoming supply services, the type of supply (single phase or three phase) and nominal voltage (230V or 400V)
- type of earthing supply system and earthing arrangements; types of protective device; ratings of devices.

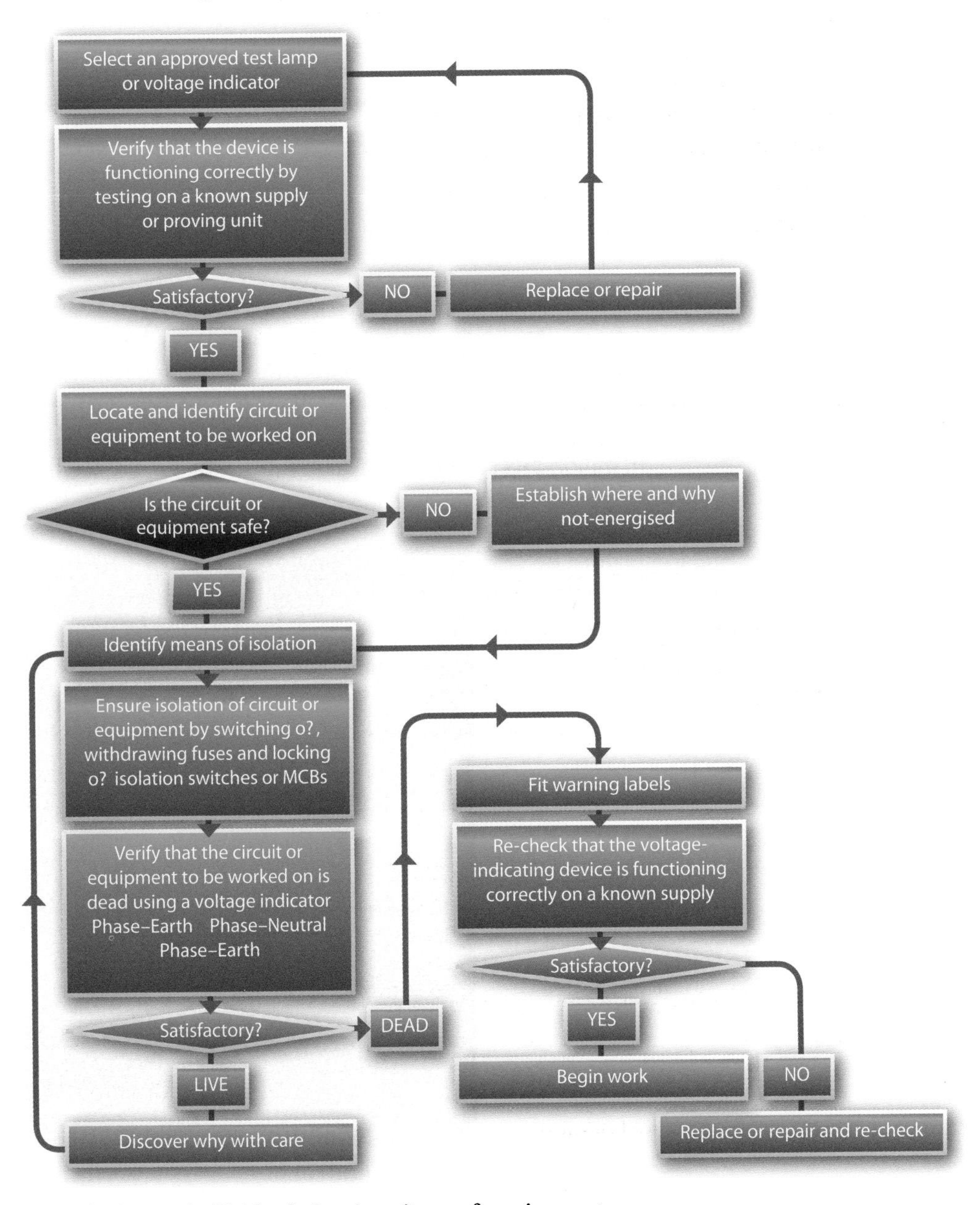

▲ Isolating an individual circuit or item of equipment

A B C D E F G H I J K L M N O P Q R S T U V W X Y Z

- distribution board schedules
- location drawings
- design and manufacturer's data.

It is important to ensure that there is no supply to the suspected fault section before attempting to correct the problem. The Joint Industry Board for the Electrical Contracting Industry publishes a safe isolating procedure for proceeding with tests and maintenance.

fault protection device

A device installed into a circuit to protect the cables and installation from damage should a fault occur. The protection is provided by ample *fuses, circuit breakers* or *residual current devices (RCDs)*.

FELV (functional extra low voltage)

See *ELV (extra low voltage)*

FET

See *Field effect transistor*

fibre optic cable

A cable used by organisations running large computer, telephone and television networks to transmit digital pulses of laser light. The fibres in fibre optic cable are fine silica glass which acts as a mirror, bouncing the light impulses down the cable. Approximately 10 billion bits of information are transmitted every second. Tight bending of the insulated cable may break the fragile inner core or cores, and joints must be made using special tools, making sure never to look at the end of cable as the light emitted is blinding.

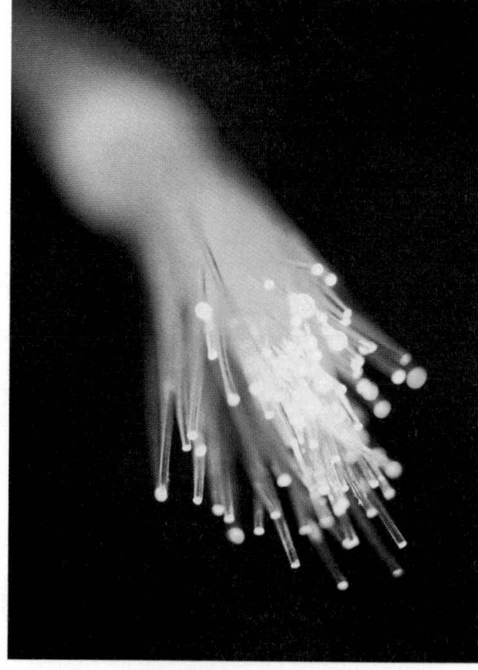

▲ Fibre optic cable

field effect transistor (FET)

A semiconductor device used in the manufacture of memories, microprocessors, calculators and digital watches. The FET has a channel of n-type semiconductor material with connections to the source (S) and the drain (D). A third connection at the gate (G) is made of p-type material to control the n-channel current. There are two types of FET: the junction gate field effect transistor (JUGFET or JFET) and the metal oxide semiconductor field effect transistor (MOSFET). The benefits of FETs are:

- unipolar – operation depends on the flow of majority current carriers only
- simple to manufacture, needs very little space
- input resistance very high – more than 10 MΩ
- low electrical noise levels; stable in temperature change.

Disadvantages of FETs include:

- prone to internal damage from static due to input *impedance*
- low voltage gain for a given bandwidth, although this is useful in applications such as radio and television
- slow switch from fully on to fully off.

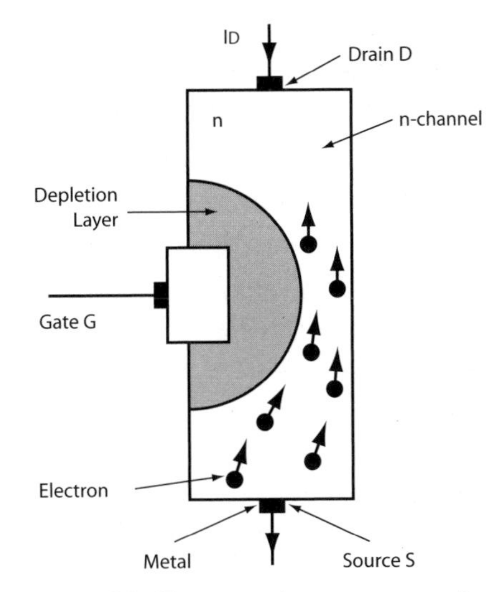

▲ Field effect transistor construction

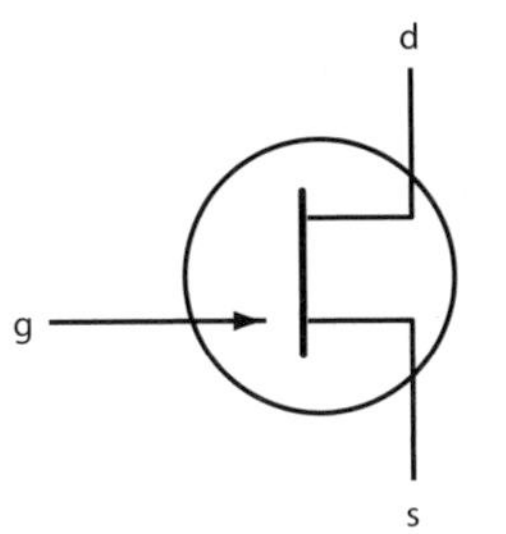

▲ Field effect transistor symbol

A
B
C
D
E
F
G
H
I
J
K
L
M
N
O
P
Q
R
S
T
U
V
W
X
Y
Z

field strength

The strength of the magnetic flux field (H) around a magnet or current-carrying conductor, measured in teslas (T).

See *Flux density*

filter circuit

A combination of *choke smoothing* and *capacitor smoothing* used to remove the ripple in the waveform of a *current*. One type of filter circuit is the capacitor input filter, which smoothes the waveform to the solid line from the original dotted line waveform.

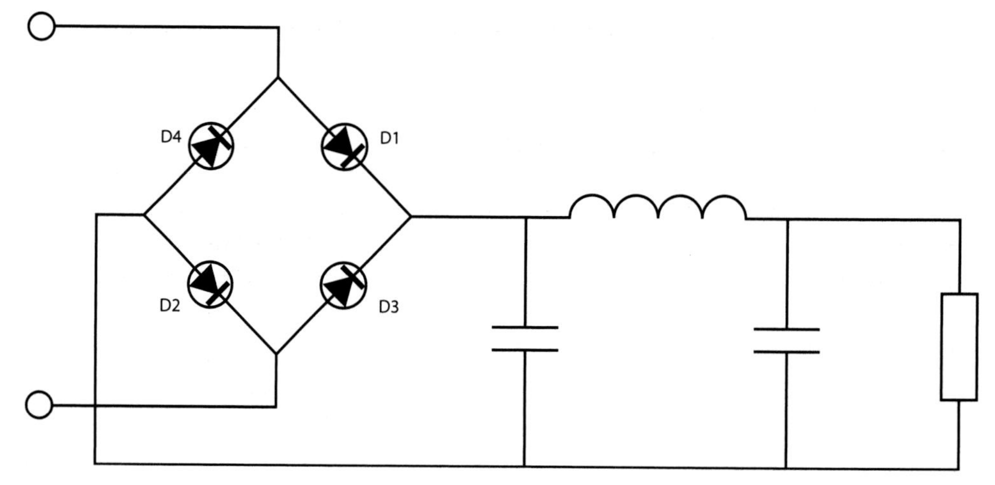

▲ Capacitor input filter

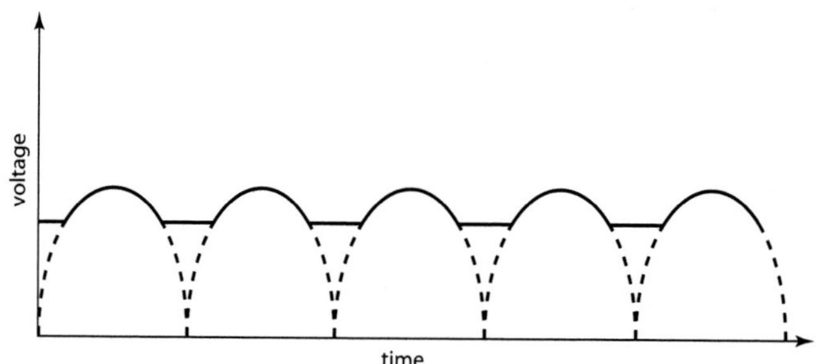

▲ Capacitor waveform

fire alarm system

A system designed to raise an alarm in the event of fire. It should operate for a sufficient period of time to enable all personnel to move away from the fire to a safe location.

BS 5839 Part 1 classifies fire detection and alarm systems as:

- Type M – no automatic detection (a person has to break a glass to operate the alarm sounders)

- Type L – automatic detection and alarm systems for the protection of life
- Type P – automatic detection and alarm systems for the protection of property.

In addition to BS 5839 Part 1, BS 7671, manufacturers' instructions and local government requirements apply to the correct installation of fire detection and alarm systems. Fire detection and alarm circuits must be segregated with a dedicated circuit to supply mains power to the fire alarm control panel.

See *Regulations*

flash point

The minimum temperature at which a material gives off sufficient vapour to form an explosive atmosphere.

Fleming's left-hand (motor) rule

An easy method for working out the relationship between the direction of movement of a *conductor*, *magnetic field* and *current* flow. The first finger, the second finger and the thumb of the left hand are held at right angles to each other as shown in the diagram. If the first finger is pointing in the direction of the magnetic field (N to S), and the second finger is pointing in the direction of the current in the conductor, then the thumb shows the direction in which the conductor will move.

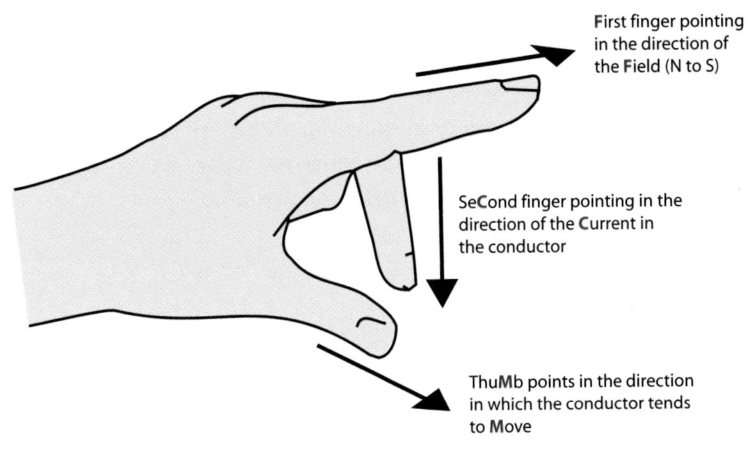

▲ Fleming's left-hand (motor) rule

flexible cables and cords – inspection and testing

These should be inspected for general damage or deterioration and for defects in the terminations and anchor points. Flexible cables and cords should also be checked for adequate mechanical or thermal protection.

A
B
C
D
E
F
G
H
I
J
K
L
M
N
O
P
Q
R
S
T
U
V
W
X
Y
Z

fluorescent lamp

A low-pressure mercury vapour lamp which has a phosphor-coated glass tube filled with gas, such as krypton or argon, and a small amount of mercury vapour, with a sealed set of oxide-coated *cathodes* at each end. A high *voltage*, achieved using a *transformer* or *choke*, is applied across the ends of the tube. This heats the cathodes forming a cloud of electrons and *ionisation* of the gas along the length of the tube. The arc strikes and is maintained in the mercury. This emits a small amount of visible light and a large quantity of ultraviolet which is absorbed by the phosphor coating and transformed into visible light.

See *Quick start circuit*; *Semi-resonant starter*; *Stroboscopic effect*; *Starter – fluorescent lamps*; *Thermal starter circuit*

flux density

The strength and extent of a *magnetic field*, calculated by counting the lines of magnetic flux within a given area and is measured in webers per square metre or tesla. The formula for calculating flux density is:

$$B = \frac{\Phi}{a}$$

Where:

B = flux density

Φ = magnetic flux in webers

a = cross sectional area in m^2

force

A push or pull, such as the wind, or gravity, acting on a body; if the push or pull is greater than the opposing force, the object will move or change shape. Force is measured in newtons and may be calculated using the formula:

Force (N) = mass × acceleration

former

A cylinder or cube of material wound with wire in a helix to produce coils or windings.

FP 200 cable

A type of cable with integrated mechanical protection. The special glands and seals produced by the manufacturers for use with this cable should always be used. FP 200 Gold is used in fixed installations in dry or damp premises where prolonged operation is required in the event of fire, for example *fire alarm* and *emergency lighting* circuits. It has solid or stranded copper *conductors* covered with Insudite – a type of *insulation* resistant to fire damage – and a laminated aluminium-tape electrostatic screen. The sheath on this cable is a thermoplastic low-smoke, zero-halogen sheath, which provides a barrier against moisture.

▲ FP200 cable

frequency (f)

The rate at which alternating (*a.c.*) current completes one cycle from zero to positive maximum, to negative maximum and back to zero, measured in hertz (Hz).

fuse

An *overcurrent protection* device designed to operate within specified limits. A fuse disconnects the supply automatically in the event of an *overload current*, *short circuit* or *earth fault*.

See *BS 88 high breaking capacity (HBC) fuse*; *BS 1361/1362 cartridge fuses*; *BS 3036 fuse*; *Discrimination*; *Neozed fuse*; *Type 'D' fuse*

fused plug

The simplest form of *isolator* used for portable appliances. When unplugged from the socket outlet the fused plug provides complete isolation from the supply.

fused spur

A spur connected to a ring final circuit through a fused connection; there may be an unlimited number of fused spurs on a circuit. The fuse should be less than 13 A and related to the current carrying capacity of the spur cable. Sockets wired from a fused spur should have *conductors* which are a minimum of 1.5 mm^2 for rubber or PVC-insulated cables with copper conductors and 1 mm^2 for *MICC mineral-insulated copper cables*.

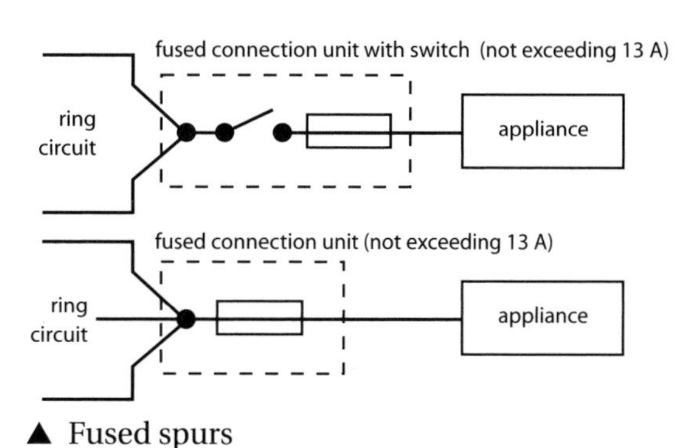

▲ Fused spurs

fusing factor

The ratio of the minimum *current* that will cause a *protective device* to trip, to the current that the protective device can sustain without tripping.

Gantt chart

A type of *bar chart* showing activities against time; it is used to plan and monitor project progress. In the diagram, the red bars show the planned time for each activity and the blue bars show the actual progress at the end of day 3.

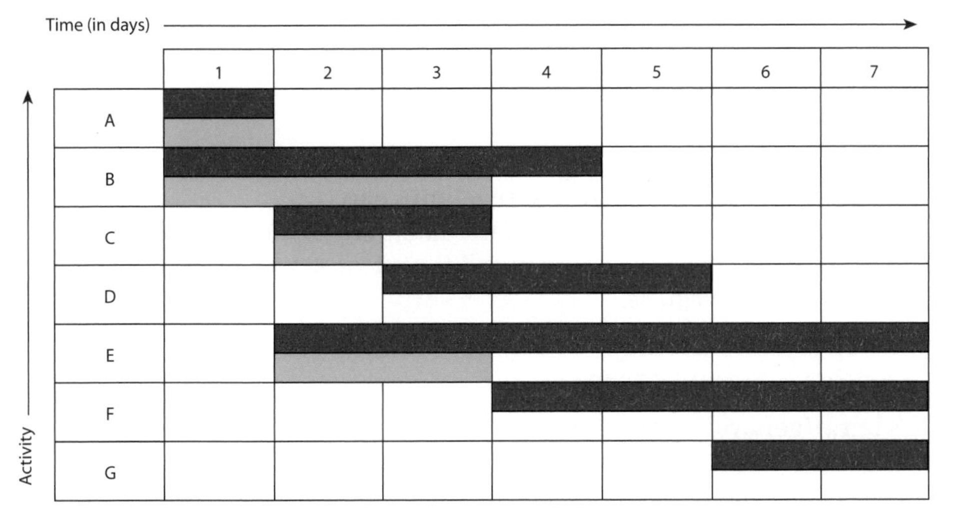

▲ Gantt chart

general lighting service lamp

See *GLS lamp/general lighting service lamp*

A B C D E F G H I J K L M N O P Q R S T U V W X Y Z

generation of electricity

Most electricity is generated in power stations where high-pressure steam is forced onto the vanes of a steam turbine, which rotates the alternator. A variety of energy sources can be used to heat the water, including coal, gas, oil and nuclear power.

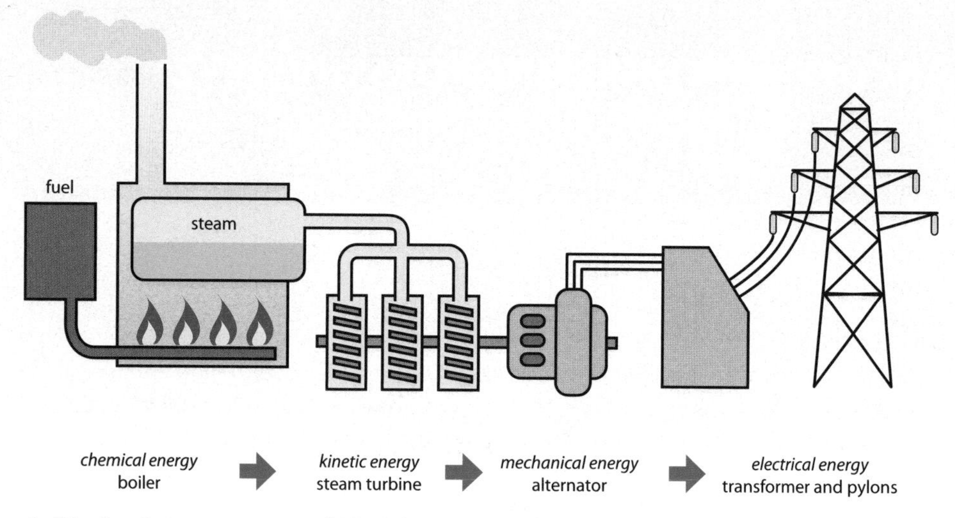

▲ The basic components of electricity generation systems

generator

See *a.c. generator*; *d.c. generator*

GES lamp cap/Goliath Edison Screw lamp cap

Most lamps have a bayonet-fitting, screw-fitting or plug-fitting cap to attach the lamp to the fitting. The GES lamp cap is used for 300 W and 500 W lamps in floodlighting installations.

glow-type starter circuit

See *Starter – fluorescent lamps*

GLS lamp/general lighting service lamp

An incandescent lamp, or 'light bulb', in which a fine tungsten-wire coiled filament is connected across an electrical supply and heats up to white heat (2500–2900°C), giving out light. The glass bulb contains no oxygen and is either a vacuum or filled with an inert gas such as nitrogen or argon. This method of producing light is not very efficient, producing between 10 and 18 lumens per watt. High-wattage lamps have a small integral fuse within the body of the lamp to prevent damage when the filament fails.

One advantage of the GLS lamp is that it can be dimmed easily. The tungsten filament is wired in series with a *triac*. The gate circuit has a *diac* connected in series and a variable *resistor* which allows the light output of the lamp to be controlled from zero to full brightness: an increase in the resistor value increases the time that the *capacitor* takes to reach the charge level required to pass current into the diac circuit and a reduction in the resistance allows the triac to switch on faster in each half-cycle.

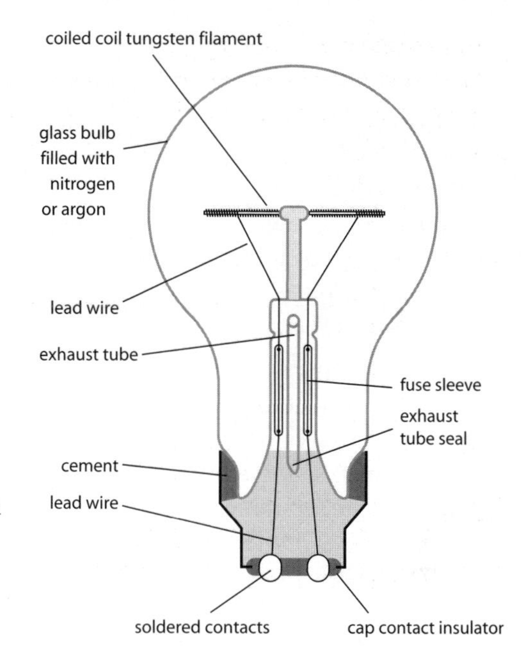

▲ GLS lamp

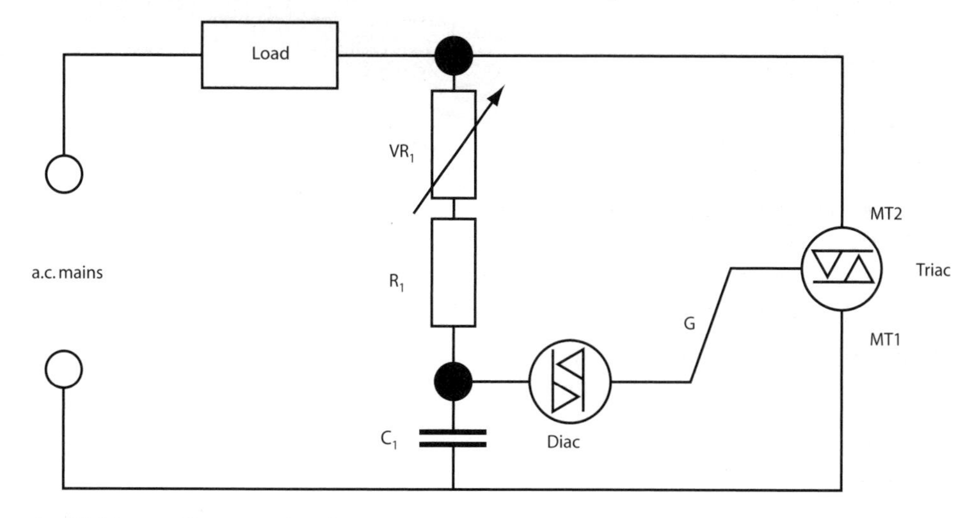

▲ GLS lamp dimmer circuit

A
B
C
D
E
F
G
H
I
J
K
L
M
N
O
P
Q
R
S
T
U
V
W
X
Y
Z

Goliath Edison Screw lamp cap

See *GES lamp cap*

gripple

A system for supporting a *cable basket* and similar loads using mini Tirfor jacks which can be tensioned to the correct position. The whole gripple is released using a special key.

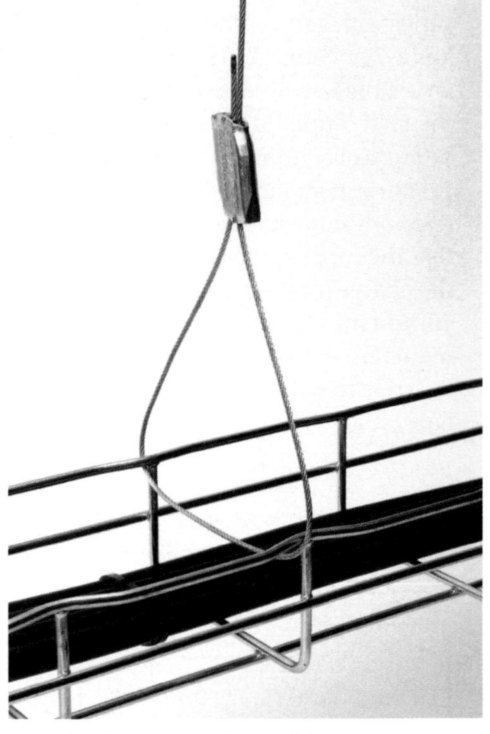

▲ Gripple-supporting cable tray

grouping factors

One of the correction factors for cables to prevent them overheating (see Tables 4B1, 4B2 and 4B3). The grouping factor is applied, if it is not possible to keep cables separate, to reduce overheating. Grouped cables are less able to cool down. The method of installation of grouped cables also affects the correction factor to be used.

Guidance Note GS 38

A document published by the Health and Safety Executive giving guidance on electrical testing and safe isolation procedures.

Guidance Notes

These are the seven guides to the IEE Wiring *Regulations* (BS 7671) published by the Institution of Electrical Engineers:

1 Selection and erection of equipment
2 Isolation and switching
3 Inspection and testing
4 Protection against fire
5 Protection against electric shock
6 Protection against overcurrent
7 Special locations.

half saddle

See *Strap saddle*

hand-operated star-delta starter

A method used for starting a three-phase *squirrel cage motor*. The windings are connected in a star formation for accelerating the rotor from standstill. When the motor reaches a steady speed the operator must move the handle to the run position quickly, then the windings will be connected in a delta formation. This is an inexpensive starter suited to motors with light loads.

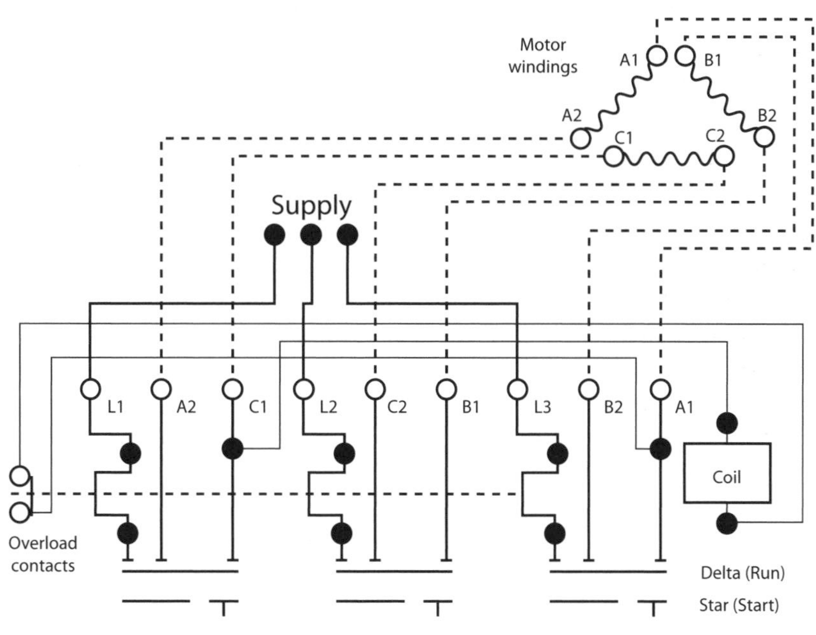

▲ Hand-operated star-delta connection

A B C D E F G H I J K L M N O P Q R S T U V W X Y Z

hazard

Anything that can cause harm, for example electricity, chemicals, working at a height or in a confined space. Electrical hazards include:

- contact with live electrical parts (230 V *a.c.* can cause death)
- fires caused by electrical faults
- electrical ignition of a flammable or explosive atmosphere
- wet conditions, where unsuitable equipment can become live.

hazardous areas

See *Explosive areas – installations*

HBC fuse

See *BS 88 high breaking capacity fuse*

Health and Safety at Work Act (1974) (HASAWA)

All employers are covered by the HASAWA, which places specific duties on both employers and employees to ensure that workplaces are safe. Non-compliance can result in fines. Employers are required to:

- provide and maintain safe plant and systems of work
- ensure safe use, handling, storage and transport of articles and substances
- provide information, instruction, training and supervision on Health and Safety at work
- provide safe access and exits
- provide adequate facilities and arrangements for welfare at work.

Employees are required to:

- take care at work for personal Health and Safety and the Health and Safety of others
- never interfere with or misuse anything provided for Health and Safety reasons
- co-operate with the employer on Health and Safety matters
- report Health and Safety problems, especially those presenting a serious danger.

high-frequency circuits

These are 30,000 Hz circuits used for *fluorescent lamp*; after the cost of installation they save between 10 and 30 per cent of electricity costs and have no flicker or *stroboscopic effect*. The lamp is brighter and the *ballast inductance* shuts down automatically on lamp failure. Supply cables installed in the luminaire cannot run next to the leads connected to the ballast output terminals, as this may cause interference.

high-risk-task area lighting

One form of *emergency lighting* provided to ensure that lighting is available for people involved in hazardous processes, so that the correct shut-down procedures can be carried out.

high voltage d.c. (HVDC) system

A system used to connect two *a.c.* regions of a power-distribution grid, especially across long distance, where the cost of HVDC conductors offsets the cost of a.c./ d.c. conversions.

highway power supplies and street furniture

These represent one of the special locations which present a greater risk of electric shock to members of the public and animals. Highway power supplies and street furniture include, for example, electrical installations for advertisements, bus shelters, *CCTV*, street and pavement lights, and traffic signs.

hygroscopic

Having a tendancy to absorb moisture.

hypotenuse

The longest side in a right-angle triangle, directly opposite the right angle. See *Cosine*; *Power factor*

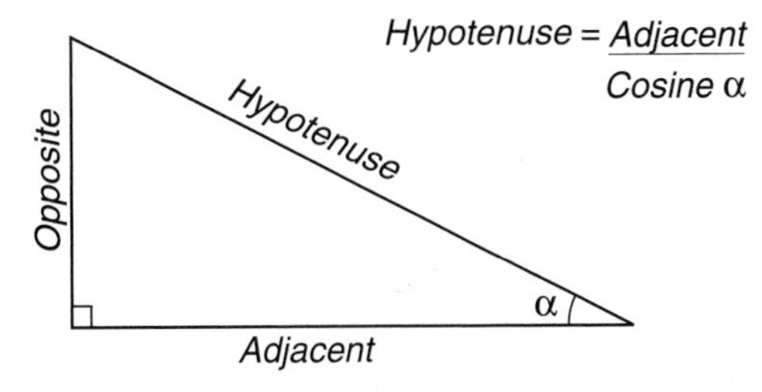

▲ Hypotenuse

A B C D E F G H I J K L M N O P Q R S T U V W X Y Z

A
B
C
D
E
F
G
H
I
J
K
L
M
N
O
P
Q
R
S
T
U
V
W
X
Y
Z

hysteresis

A lag in the effect of a change of force, for example the magnetism in an object changes in response to changes in the *magnetic field*, but the response is not instantaneous. The hysteresis loop starts with an unmagnetised ferrous material (A), as the field strength increases, the *flux density* of the material increases, up to saturation point (B). The dotted line from A to B is the initial magnetisation curve. When the field strength is reduced the flux density in the material reduces slowly, so that when the field strength is zero at C, the flux density of the material will still be a finite value: this is called the *remanence*. The flux density in the material will not reduce to zero unless the field is reversed; this is called the *coercivity*.

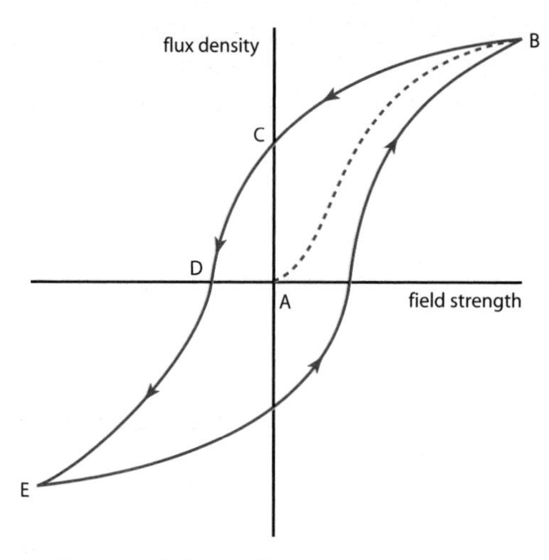

▲ Hysteresis loop diagram

IC

See *Integrated circuit*

IEE Guidance Notes

See *Guidance Notes*

illuminance

A measure of the amount of visible light that falls on a given surface. Illuminance is measured in lux (lx), that is, lumens per square metre.

immersion heater

A method used to heat large tanks (over 130 litres) of water. The heating element incorporates a stem-type *thermostat* to control water temperature and is fitted into the tank with a timer or on/off switch attached on the outside. It is very important to ensure that the exposed and extraneous conductive parts are bonded to earth correctly and that the correct size of cable is used for full load current. Heatproof flexible cable must be used to connect to the heating element. In a domestic property the immersion heater must have a dedicated *fuse* or *MCB* in the consumer unit and a double-pole *isolator* fitted next to the water tank. Some systems have two heating elements, one of which operates on night-time supply.

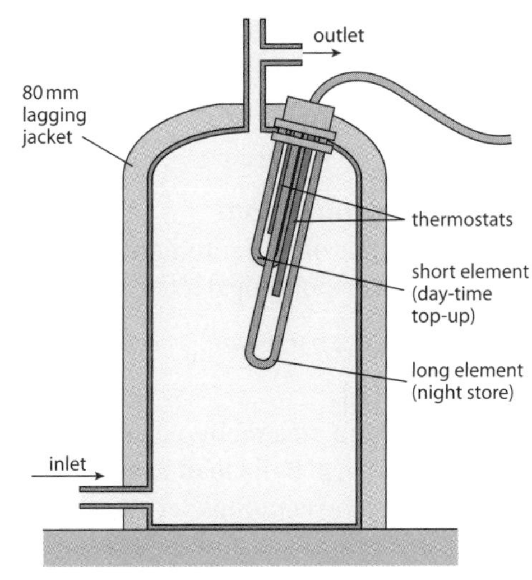

▲ Dual-element immersion heater, hot water

A
B
C
D
E
F
G
H
I
J
K
L
M
N
O
P
Q
R
S
T
U
V
W
X
Y
Z

impedance (Z)

The total amount of opposition to the flow of *a.c.* in a circuit. Impedance includes resistance, inductance and capacitance, and is measured in ohms.

See *Capacitance*; *Inductance*; *Resistance*

in phase

This is an electricity supply where the *current* and the *voltage* alternate at the same time.

incandescent lamp

See *GLS lamp*; *Tungsten halogen lamp*

indicator lamp

A lamp operated by a two-way switch and used, for example, to show that a room is occupied.

indirect contact protection

The protection against persons or livestock having contact with exposed conductive parts, which could become live under fault conditions. Exposed conductive parts include metal *trunking*, metal *conduit* and the metal casing of appliances. BS 7671 lists the methods of protection against indirect contact:

- earthed *equipotential bonding* and automatic disconnection of supply
- use of class II equipment
- non-conducting location
- earth-free local equipotential bonding
- electrical separation.

Separate extra low voltage (SELV) is used for protection against both direct and indirect contact. Requirements for this type of system include:

- isolated source of supply
- electrical separation
- no connection with earth, exposed conductive parts or the protective conductors of other systems.

See *Direct contact protection*; *ELV*; *Regulations*

indirectly proportional

Two properties or measurements are indirectly proportional if an increase in one causes a corresponding decrease in the other.

See *Directly proportional*

inductance (L)

The opposition created by a changing *current* in a *magnetic field* which induces a reverse *voltage*. If the load in a circuit has windings, such as a motor or *transformer*, the windings set up an induced *e.m.f.* in the opposite direction to the applied voltage and the current falls behind the voltage. No power is consumed but the voltage and current are not perfectly linked. The SI unit of inductance is known as the henry (H) and is the rate of change of current in a circuit of 1 amp per second, which produces an induced *electromotive force* of 1 volt. Inductance within a circuit is called *self-inductance*; inductance in a different circuit within the same magnetic field is called *mutual inductance*.

induction motor

An *a.c.* motor with shortened wire loops on a rotating *armature*. The interaction of the two *magnetic fields* in the *stator* (stationary) coils produces electrical energy which is transferred inductively to the rotating armature, causing it to rotate. This is the simplest and most common type of a.c. motor.

inductive circuit

A circuit which includes components with windings which set up an induced *e.m.f.* in the opposite direction to the applied voltage. The voltage increases in the first part of the cycle. The energy is stored in the *inductor* and fed back into the circuit in the second part of the cycle, when the voltage decreases.

inductive reactance (X_L)

The limiting effect on the flow of an *a.c.* produced by an *inductor* and measured in ohms and calculated using the formula:

$$X_L = 2\pi fL$$

where:

X_L = inductive reactance (ohms – Ω)

f = supply frequency (hertz – Hz)

L = circuit inductance (henries – H)

An example of a sine wave used to represent an inductive circuit.

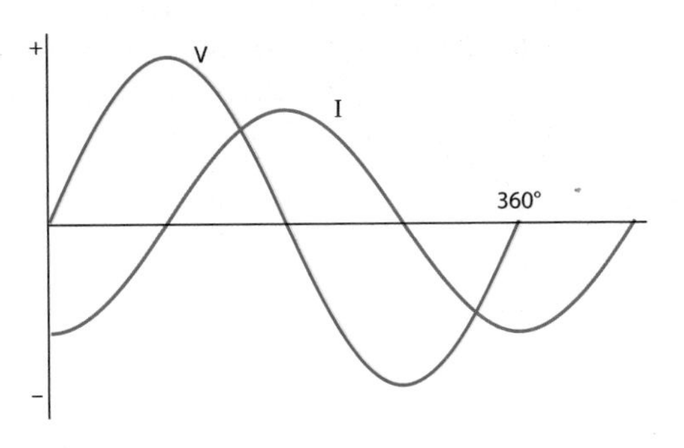

If we represented this as a phasor diagram we end up with

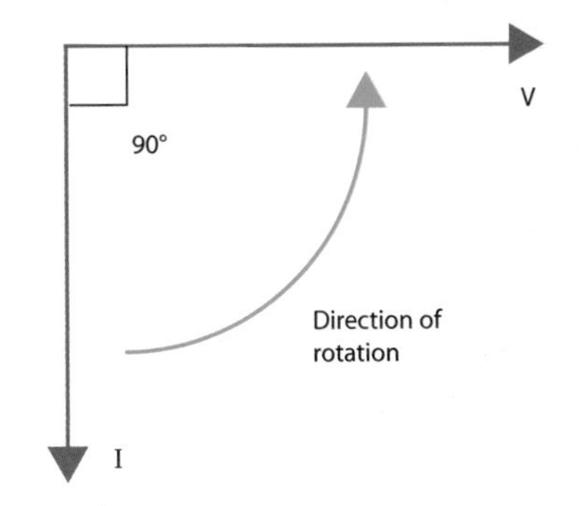

▲ Sine wave and phasor diagrams for an inductive circuit

A B C D E F G H I J K L M N O P Q R S T U V W X Y Z

inductor

A component used to provide a required amount of *inductance* in a circuit. The energy stored in the *magnetic field* of an inductor is returned to the source when the *current* changes direction. The value most common inductors ranges from 0.1 microhenry (0.1 μH) to 10 henries (10 H).

inertia switch

A component of perimeter protection for an *intruder alarm system* which detects any vibrations produced when a door or window is forced open. The switch sends a signal to the alarm panel which activates the sounder. The inertia switch usually operates on a 12 volt *d.c.* supply.

infrared

The non-visible electromagnetic radiation that humans sense as heat.

infrared heater

A direct acting space heater with an element (iconel-sheathed or nickel-chrome spiral) housed in a glass silica tube and mounted in front of a highly polished surface. Infrared heaters are available from 500 W to 3 kW.

infrared source and sensor

An *infrared* beam is projected from a *light emitting diode (LED)*, but the beam is not visible. The diagram shows housings for infrared sources and sensors used for security alarms. Infrared sensors react to the beam depending on the application, for example television remote controls.

See *Passive infrared (PIR) sensor*

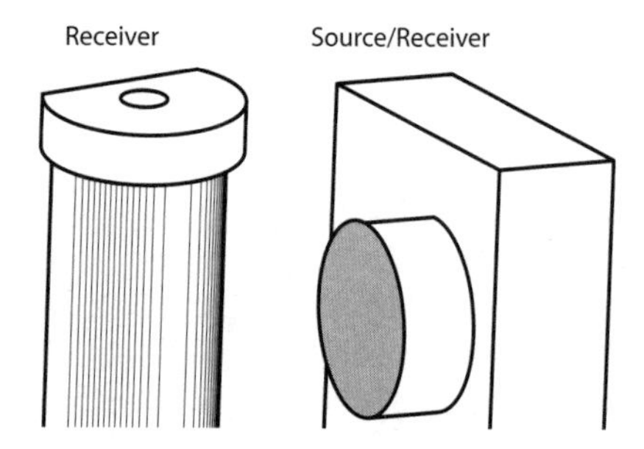

▲ Housings for infrared source output and sensors for security alarms

initial inspection

An initial inspection of an installation should be conducted to ensure:

- correct use of equipment and materials
- correct selection and installation of components and sections
- no visible sign of damage or defective parts
- suitability for environmental conditions.

The following items should be checked:

- connection of conductors
- identification of conductors
- cable routes
- current carrying capacity
- verification of polarity
- accessories and equipment

- selection and erection to minimise the spread of fire
- protection against electric shock.

Refer to the IEE Wiring *Regulations* (BS 7671), the IEE On-Site Guide and IEE Guidance Note 3 for further information.

See *Regulations*; *Guidance Notes*

initial verification

Every electrical installation should be inspected and tested to ensure that the requirements of the BS regulations (BS 7671 Part 7) have been met and that the installation complies with the designer's requirements.

inspection checklist

A document produced to ensure that all the requirements of the *Regulations* have been met. Different installations may require different checklists.

Joint Boxes (tick if satisfactory)	
All joint boxes comply with the appropriate British Standard.	
Joints accessible for inspection where required.	
All conductors correctly connected.	
Joints protected against mechanical damage.	

Wiring Accessories (General Requirements) (tick if satisfactory)	
All accessories comply with the appropriate British Standard.	
Boxes and other enclosures securely fastened.	
Metal boxes and enclosures correctly earthed.	
Flush boxes not projecting above surface of wall.	
No sharp edges which could cause damage to cable insulation.	
Non-sheathed cables not exposed outside box or enclosure.	
Conductors correctly identified.	
Bare protective conductors sleeved green and yellow.	
All terminals tight and contain all strands of stranded conductor.	
Cord grips correctly used to prevent strain on terminals.	
All accessories of adequate current rating.	
Accessories suitable for all conditions likely to be encountered.	

▲ Inspection checklist (continued)

Socket Outlet (tick if satisfactory)	
Comply with appropriate British Standard.	
Mounting height above floor or working surface is correct.	
All sockets have correct polarity.	
Sockets not installed in bathroom or shower room (unless shaver type socket).	
Sockets not within 2.5 m of a shower in a room other than a bathroom.	
Sockets controlled by a switch if the supply is direct current.	
Sockets correctly protected where floor mounted.	
Circuit protective conductor connected directly to the earthing terminal of the socket outlet on a sheathed wiring installation.	
Earthing tail provided from the earthed metal box to the earthing terminal of the socket outlet.	
Socket outlets not used to supply a water heater with un-insulated elements.	

Lighting Controls (tick if satisfactory)	
Light switches comply with appropriate British Standard.	
Switches suitably located.	
Single-pole switches connected in phase conductor only.	
Correct colour coding of conductors.	
Correct earthing of metal switch plates.	
Switches out of reach of a person using bath or shower.	
Switches for inductive circuits (discharge lamps) de-rated as necessary.	
Switches labelled to indicate purpose where this is not obvious.	
All switches of adequate current rating.	
All controls suitable for their associated luminaire.	

▲ Inspection checklist (continued)

Lighting Points (tick if satisfactory)	
All lighting points correctly terminated in suitable accessory or fitting.	
Ceiling roses comply with appropriate British Standard.	
No more than one flexible cord unless designed for multiple pendants.	
Devices provided for supporting flex used correctly.	
All switch wires identified.	
Holes in ceiling above ceiling rose made good to prevent spread of fire.	
Ceiling roses not connected to supply exceeding 250 V.	
Flexible cords suitable for the mass suspended.	
Lamp holders comply with appropriate British Standard.	
Luminaire couplers comply with appropriate British Standard.	

Conduits (general) (tick if satisfactory)	
All inspection fittings accessible.	
Maximum number of cables not exceeded.	
Solid elbows used only as permitted.	
Conduit ends reamed and bushed.	
Adequate number of boxes.	

Conduits (general) (tick if satisfactory)	
All unused entries blanked off.	
Lowest point provided with drainage holes where required.	
Correct radius of bends to prevent damage to cables.	
Joints and scratches in metal conduit protected by painting.	

▲ Inspection checklist (continued)

A
B
C
D
E
F
G
H
I
J
K
L
M
N
O
P
Q
R
S
T
U
V
W
X
Y
Z

Circuit protective conductors (enter circuit details from specifications)	
1.	
2.	
3.	
4.	
5.	
6.	
7.	
8.	

▲ Inspection checklist (continued)

Inspection Schedule

A document which lists the inspection requirements of BS *Regulation* 712-01-03, and which, when completed, is attached to the *Electrical Installation Certificate*.

inspection/testing

Inspection and testing should be conducted:

- when alterations or additions are completed
- on all newly completed installations (initial inspection)
- at regular intervals to ascertain any damage, wear and tear, corrosion, excessive electrical loading, ageing and environmental influences (*periodic inspection and testing*)
- if there is a change in use of the premises
- if there is a significant change in the electrical loading of the installation
- if there is a possibility that damage may have been caused to the installation.

An inspection should cover:

- connection of conductors
- identification of each conductor of non-flexible cables
- identification of flexible cable and cord
- routing of cables
- current carrying capacity
- verification of polarity
- accessories and equipment – correct connection
- selection and erection to minimise the spread of fire
- *direct contact protection*
- *indirect contact protection*
- protective devices.

A B C D E F G H I J K L M N O P Q R S T U V W X Y Z

- documentation
- warning notices.

See *Guidance Note GS38*; *Initial inspection*; *Periodic inspection and testing*

instantaneous water heater

An appliance that heats water as required by controlling the flow of water through a small water tank with internal heating elements. The slower the water flow, the hotter the water becomes. Some electric showers operate on this principle. The water heater must be supplied through a dedicated *fuse* or *MCB* in the consumer unit. A double-pole *isolator* must be installed near the shower.

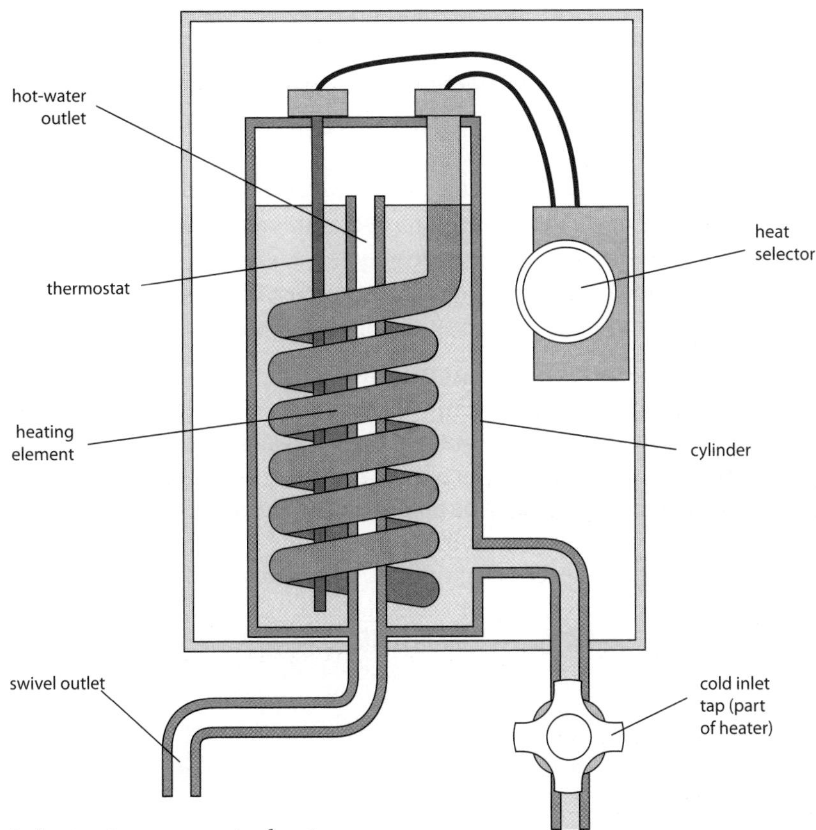

▲ Instantaneous water heater

instrument transformer

This is a double-wound *transformer* used in conjunction with measuring instruments when measuring high *current* and *voltage* in certain power systems.

instrumentation

The installation of process control and measurement systems, with components such as flow meters, pressure and temperature gauges, pumps, valves and level switches. Instrumentation is required for industries such as water, chemical, pharmaceutical and manufacturing.

A B C D E F G H I J K L M N O P Q R S T U V W X Y Z

insulated gate bipolar transistor (IGBT)

A *transistor* used in the speed control of *a.c. induction motors*. The *a.c.* is converted to *d.c.* and then back to a.c. using insulated gate bipolar transistors (IGBT), which creates a variable a.c. voltage and *frequency* output.

insulation

The use of materials with extremely good insulating properties to insulate the *conductors* of a cable from each other and from any surrounding metalwork. The insulation must be suitable for the situation, and may be one of the following types:

- PVC – tough, flexible, inexpensive, easy to work with, but cannot withstand extremes of heat and cold (BS 7671 recommends use only between 0 and 60°C).
- Synthetic rubbers (e.g. *vulcanised butyl rubber*) – withstands high temperatures; used for immersion heaters, storage heaters and boiler-house equipment.
- Magnesium oxide (mineral-insulated cables) – hygroscopic, so needs protection from damp; withstands high temperatures and mechanical damage.
- Phenol-formaldehyde – thermosetting polymer, can withstand high temperatures; used for socket outlets, plug tops, switches and consumer units.

insulation resistance – measurement and tests

Insulation resistance tests are used to verify the correct insulation of *conductors*, electrical accessories and equipment, and that electrical and protective conductors have effective insulation and are not *short circuited*. The meters used to measure insulation resistance must be able to withstand and record high values (the test voltage required is given in BS 7671 Table 71A). When measuring insulation resistance, disconnect all electronic devices and record the presence

Table 71A Minimum value of insulation resistance		
Circuit nominal voltage (V)	Test voltage d.c. (V)	Minimum insulation resistance (megohms)
SELV and PELV	250	0.25
Up to and including 500 V with the exception of the above systems	500	0.5
Above 500 V	1000	1.0

▲ Minimum value of insulation resistance (BS 7671)

of the equipment on the Schedule of Test Results. The installation conforms to regulations if it has an insulation resistance not less than that specified in Table 71A, with the main switchboard and each distribution circuit tested separately and with all the final circuits connected, but current-using equipment disconnected.

See *Regulations*

insulator

Material in which the atoms are tightly packed and electrons cannot move; therefore the material will not conduct an electric current.

See *Insulation*

integrated circuit (IC)

An electronic circuit, also known as a chip. The IC may have millions of electronic components on one semiconductor crystal housed within a plastic case.

intruder alarm system

A system for detecting intruders on to a property and raising an alarm. It includes *perimeter protection* (used outside the building and on doors and windows, to detect intruders before they enter the building) and *space detection* (used to detect intruders within a building).

See *Control panel*; *Inertia switch*; *Passive infrared (PIR) sensor*; *Proximity switch*; *Ultrasonic intruder alarm system*; *Warning device*

Invar

An alloy of nickel and iron having the special characteristic of an extremely low coefficient of expansion.

See *Oven thermostat*

ionisation

Loss or gain of electrons by an atom or group of atoms is known as ionisation. A loss creates a positive ion, a gain a negative ion.

See *Fluorescent lamp*

isolating transformer

A *transformer* used to isolate the secondary output from the supply. For example, the socket for an electric water heater in a bathroom should be supplied from a 1:1 safety isolating transformer. The transformer output has no connection to earth and is totally isolated from the supply. For sections of electrical installations with an increased risk of electric shock, the voltage is supplied from a safety isolating transformer and reduced to less than 50 V. This is called a separate extra low voltage (SELV) supply.

See *ELV (extra low voltage)*

A B C D E F G H I J K L M N O P Q R S T U V W X Y Z

isolation

An electrical installation, equipment or circuit must be completely isolated from the supply before starting work. BS 7671 requires that effective isolating and switching devices are suitably positioned and ready to operate. To ensure complete isolation, identify all the sources of supply and isolate each one, securing the isolation, then test that the installation, circuit or equipment is not live. Using an isolator, the isolating distance between contacts must comply with BS EN 60947-3.

See *Faults*; *Regulations*

isolator

A mechanical switching device used to cut off the electrical supply from an installation, a circuit or a piece of equipment. An isolator is an off-load device operated after the supply has been made dead and there is no load current to break. Portable appliances use the simplest form of isolator, a *fused plug*.

IT earthing system

A special earthing system where the earth path flows through a high *impedance* of 1500 ohms. It is used in quarries, telephone exchanges and some industrial processes where the consumer provides the connection to earth. The IT earthing system must not be connected to the supply company system.

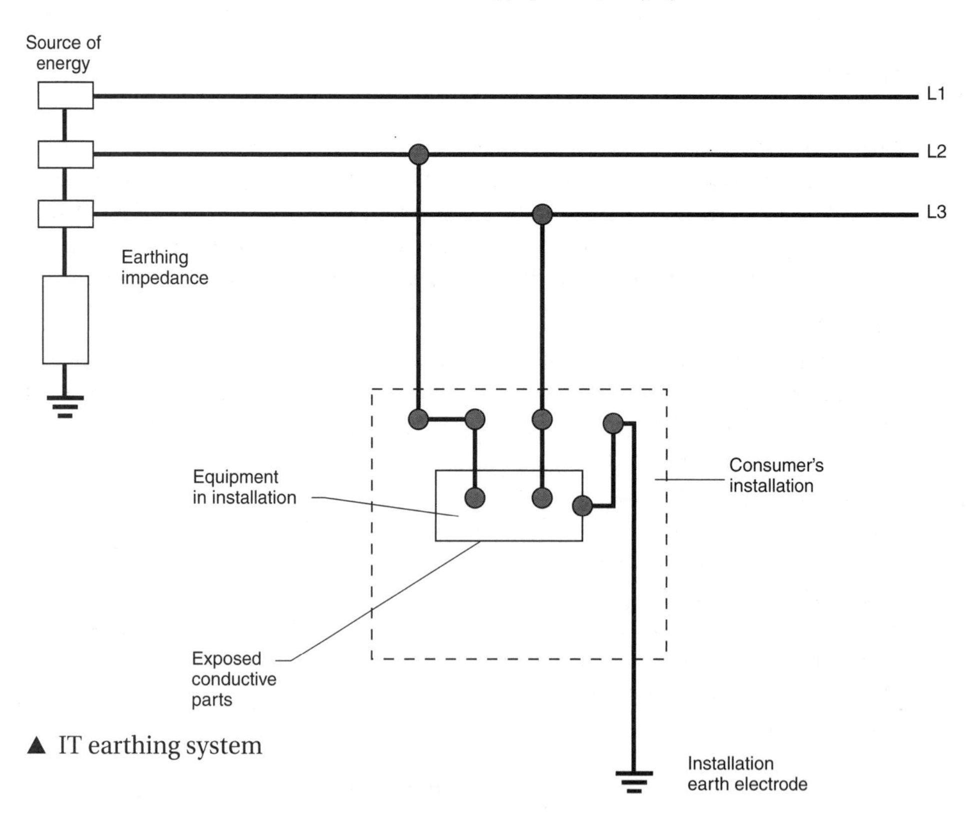

▲ IT earthing system

J

A B C D E F G H I J K L M N O P Q R S T U V W X Y Z

joints for cables

For non-flexible cables, joints may be made by soldering, brazing, welding, mechanical clamps or using a compression joint. The jointing device should be selected with reference to the size of cable and should be insulated to the level required by the voltage of the system. Where cables with different insulation are to be jointed, the *insulation* of the joint must be equal to the highest level of insulation.

See *Compression joint*; *Junction box*

joule

The unit used for measuring the amount of work done and used in the formula: work done (J) = force (N) × distance (m). Power is measured in joules per second or J/s and known as watts (W). *Electromotive force* is measured by the number of joules of work required to push one coulomb of electric charge around a circuit; the unit is joules/coulomb, commonly referred to as the volt, with one volt = one joule/coulomb.

junction box

The method used to connect cables on lighting or socket-outlet circuits. The selected junction box must have a suitable *current* rating and the correct number of terminals. When wiring junction boxes, make sure that: cables do not cross inside the box and the lid fits easily; enough slack is left inside the junction box to prevent tension on *conductors*; at least 10 mm of the protective outer sheath is taken inside the junction box; the minimum insulation is removed when terminations are made into a connector; the junction box is secured to a platform.

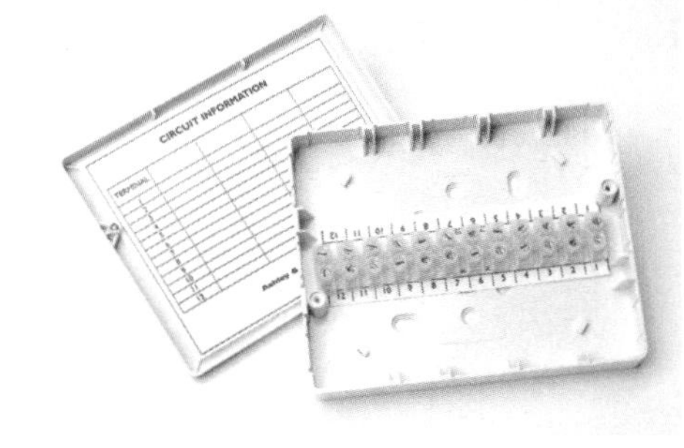

▲ Junction box

kilovolt-amps (kVA)

A measurement of 1000 volt-amps. It can be used when assessing the rating of electrical equipment to determine suitability for a given load, especially when the load is inductive. For instance, 3 kW is not necessarily the same 3 kVA – it depends on the *power factor*.

kilowatt hour (kWh)

A unit of energy whereby one kilowatt (1000 watts) of power is consumed for a period of one hour (3600 seconds). This is a more convenient measure of energy usage than the joule and is therefore used for charging customers for their electricity supply. The formulas for working this out are:

1 joule (J) = 1 watt (W) for one second (s)

1000 joules (J) = 1 kilowatt (kW) for one second

3600 s × 1000 J = 1 kW for one hour (kWh)

or 1 kWh = 3.6×10^6 J.

kinetic energy

Energy in the form of motion.

Kirchoff's Law

The sum of the *voltage* that drops around any closed loop in a network must equal zero.

labelling

Instruments used for electrical testing must be calibrated in laboratory conditions regularly – at the very least, every 12 months. Test instruments should have a calibration label stating the date of the last calibration and the date that the next one is due. An adhesive label may be placed to seal the joint in the instrument casing stating, 'If the seal is broken the calibration is void.' BS 7671 Section S14 specifies labels for circuits, *MCBs*, *RCDs*, *fuses* and isolating devices, periodic inspection notices and warning notices referring to earthing and bonding connections.

See *Marking and labelling*

lamp cap

This is used to connect lamps to the supply. There are three main types of lamp cap: bayonet-fitting, screw-fitting and plug-fitting.

See *GES lamp cap*

lamp efficacy

The lumen output of a lamp of a particular wattage; for example the efficacy of a *fluorescent lamp* is between 40 and 90 lumens per watt.

layout diagram

Scale drawings in plan view, based on an architect's drawings and showing the position for equipment, metering and control gear of a new installation. Location

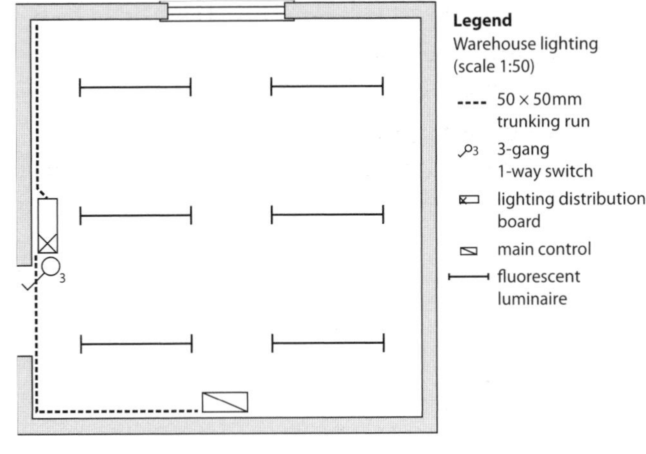

▲ Layout diagram

symbols (BS EN 60617) are used and the diagram details the sequence of control of large installations. A *materials list* can be produced from a layout diagram.

layout diagram symbols

The following symbols are used to represent various electrical components in schematic diagrams.

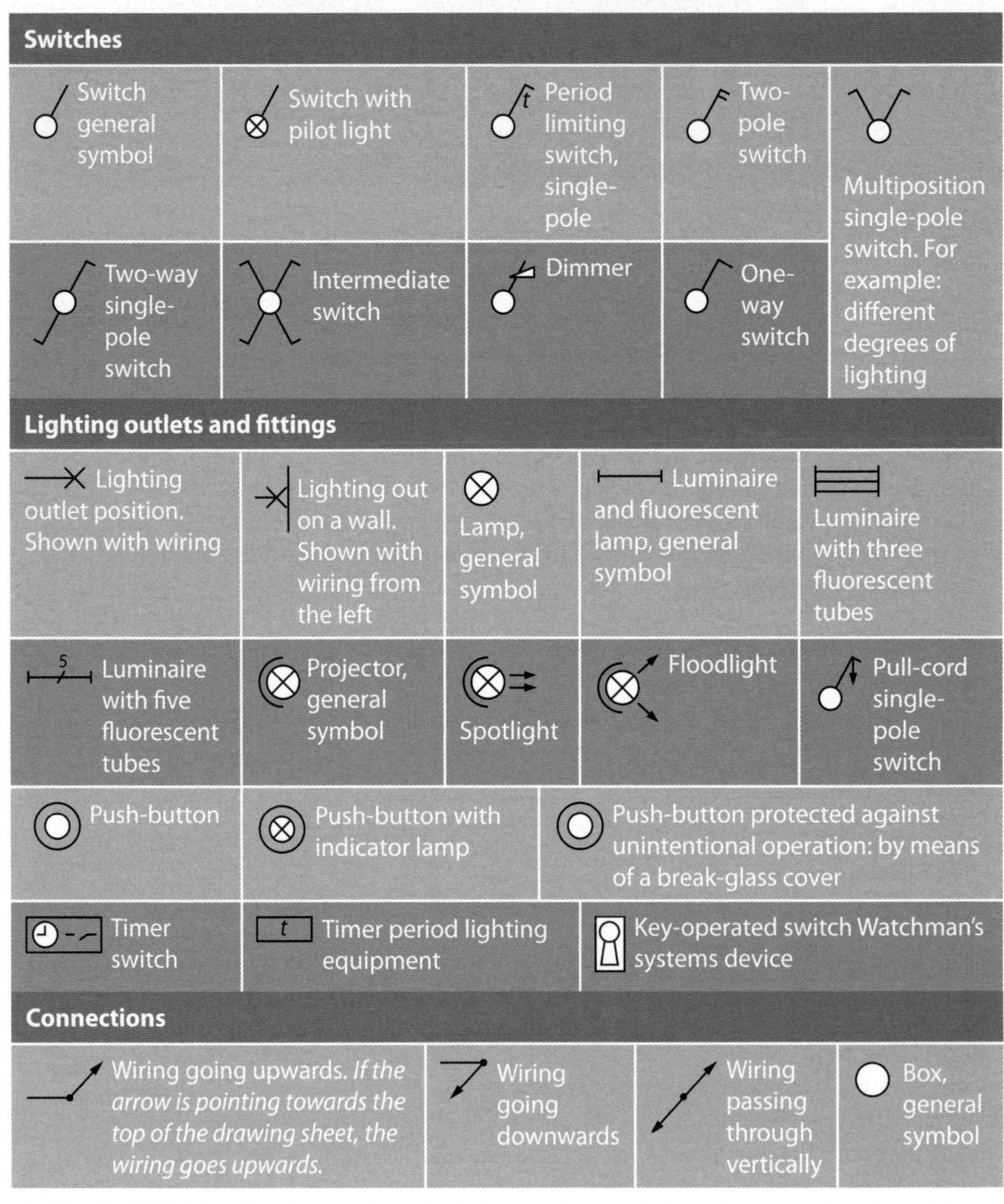

▲ BS EN 60617 lists the standard symbols for use in installation drawings (continued)

Connections (cont...)		
Connection box Junction box	Consumer's terminal service entrance equipment. *This symbol is shown with wiring*	Distribution centre/ board. *The symbol is shown with five wirings*

Sockets				
Socket outlet (power), general symbol	Multiple socket outlet (power). *The symbol is shown with three outlets*	Socket outlet (power) with protective contact	Socket output (power) with shutter	Socket outlet (power) with single-pole switch
Socket outlet (power) with interlocked switch	Socket outlet (power) with isolating transformer. For example: shaver outlet	Socket outlet (telecommunications), general symbol. Designations in accordance with relevant IEC or ISO standards, may be used to distinguish different types of outlets TP = telephone FX = fax M = microphone FM = loudspeaker TV = television TX = telex		

Miscellaneous			
Motor starter, general symbol	Direct-on-line starter with contactor for reversing the rotation of a motor	Star-delta starter	Fan. The symbol is shown with wiring
Time clock Time recorder	Hour meter Hour counter	Kilowatt-hour meter	

▲ BS EN 60617 lists the standard symbols for use in installation drawings

LED

See *Light emitting diode (LED)*

light emitting diode (LED)

A *p–n junction* especially made with semiconducting material. When a current as small as 10 mA flows through the LED, light is produced. If the diode is reverse biased then no light is emitted.

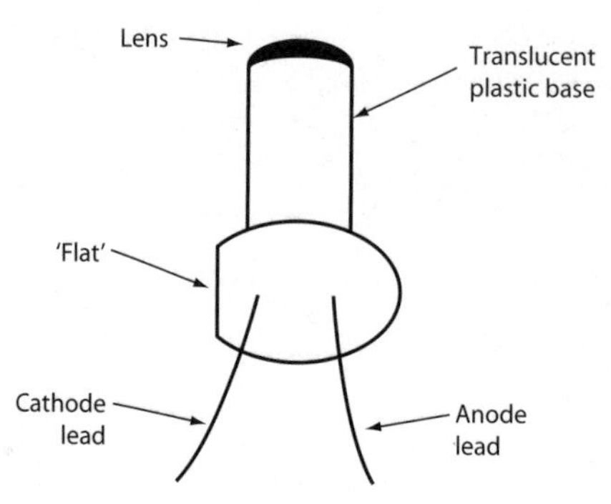

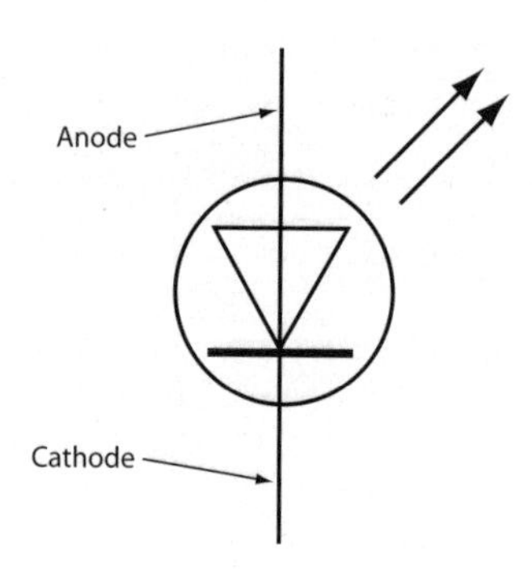

▲ Light emitting diode

lighting circuits

Circuits which may have many switching arrangements. The main ones are one-way switching, two-way switching and intermediate switching. For wiring in *conduit* and trunking, PVC single-core insulated cables are used. The phase or live conductor is taken directly to the first switch and looped from switch to switch for the rest of the lighting circuit. The neutral conductor is taken directly to the luminaire and then looped to rest of the luminaires on the lighting circuit. Each switch wire runs from the switch to the relevant luminaire.

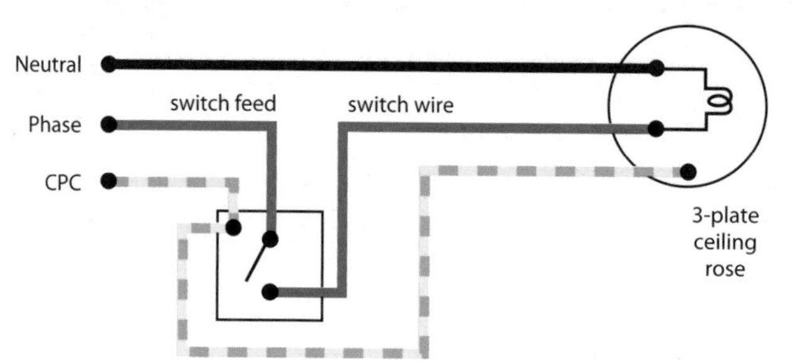

◀ One-way switching for wiring with single core cable (old wiring)

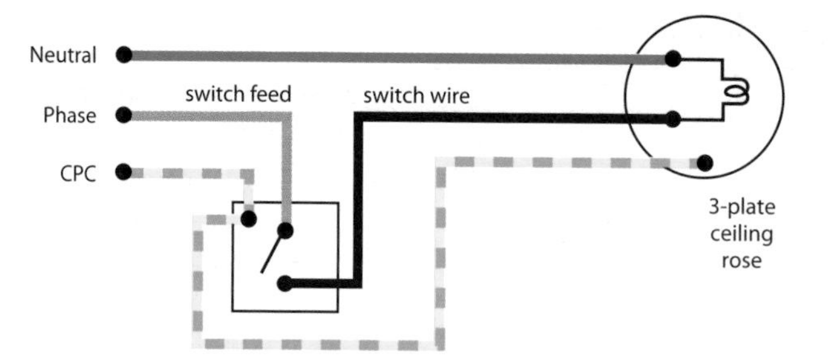

◀ One-way switching for wiring with single core cable (new wiring)

A one-way switch controls one light. One terminal of the switch receives the switch feed and the switch wire runs from the other terminal to the luminaire. The switch contact is held in place mechanically when operated allowing electricity to flow to the light.

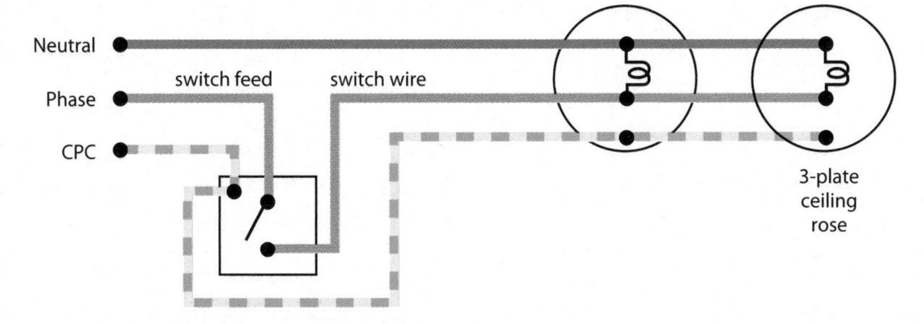

▲ Extra lighting fed from the same switch, wired in parallel (new cable colours)

Two-way switching is used to switch lights on or off from two locations, for example at the bottom and at the top of a flight of stairs. The two-way switch circuit has the switch feed running to one two-way switch, and the switch wire running from the second two-way switch to the luminaire(s). Two wires known as 'strappers' then link the two switches together. When the two two-way switches are connected each switch can either energise or de-energise the switch wire going to the light.

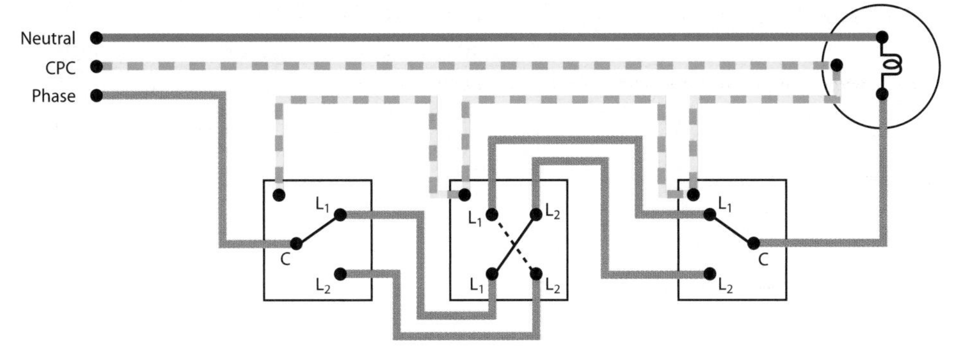

▲ Intermediate switching showing light off

Intermediate switching must be used when more than two switch locations are required, for example along a corridor. Intermediate switches are wired between the two-way switches with strapping wires so that the intermediate switch cross-connects them enabling the supply to be routed to any terminal, according to the switch contacts. The diagram shows intermediate switching arrangements for a long corridor, where the light is off.

lightning strike

A lightning strike may have a discharge current of the order of 200,000 amps. *British Standards* (Code of Practice 326: 1965 and BS 6651: 1990) cover requirements for the protection of buildings and structures from lightning by the provision of a network of copper or aluminium conductors (maximum resistance 10 ohms) installed on the roof or walls of a structure, to radio and TV masts and connected to a common point discharging to earth.

A B C D E F G H I J K L M N O P Q R S T U V W X Y Z

line current

The *current* flowing between the source and the load in any phase of a three-phase circuit.

line voltage

The *potential difference* between any two phase conductors located between the source and load in a three-phase circuit connected in star formation.

See *Star connection*

linear tungsten halogen lamp

See *Tungsten halogen lamp*

liquid crystal display (LCD)

A display made from a 'liquid crystal' material that can stop light shining through it when an electric field is applied, so appears black to the eye. It demands little power and is frequently used for digital displays in watches, calculators etc.

live conductor

A conductor carrying *current* under normal conditions, including the neutral conductor.

load balancing

Three-phase, four-wire electrical installations are designed for efficiency and economy by subdividing into balanced load categories. The maximum demand is assessed and a balanced system is achieved by spreading equipment and appliances over all three phases of the supply. Regional electricity companies require load balancing as a condition of supplying electricity.

See *Star connection*

LPG (liquid petroleum gas)

Gas used as fuel for burners, heaters and gas torches. The liquid gas is highly flammable; one litre evaporates to 250 litres of gas, which would make a highly explosive mixture with air in an enclosed space. When using LPG, study the safety data sheet, understand the emergency procedures, use the correct protective equipment and have the correct dry powder fire extinguisher available.

LSF (low smoke and fume) cables

Special insulation used on cables which, when burned, does not emit thick smoke. Usually specified in public buildings such as schools or cinemas where a swift exit is needed in the event of a fire. Such installations should not use PVC containment (e.g. PVC high impact conduit) for cables.

machine screw
A screw threaded along the whole length. It is used to join thick parts where the hole in one part is threaded and the other is a clearance hole. The BA thread range is the one most commonly used.

magnesium oxide
A *hygroscopic* white powder which forms the insulation on mineral-insulated cables. These can withstand very high temperatures and mechanical damage, but must be protected from damp.

magnet
A device which produces an external *magnetic field*, such as a *permanent magnet* or an *electromagnet*.

magnetic field
The area between the poles of a magnet where lines of force (magnetic flux) move from the north pole of the magnet to the south pole in closed loops. The lines of flux never cross, but may become distorted and will return to their original shape. The higher the number of lines of magnetic flux, the stronger the magnet. The number of lines of flux at any point in the magnetic field indicates the strength of the field or the *flux density*.

See *Electromagnetic force*

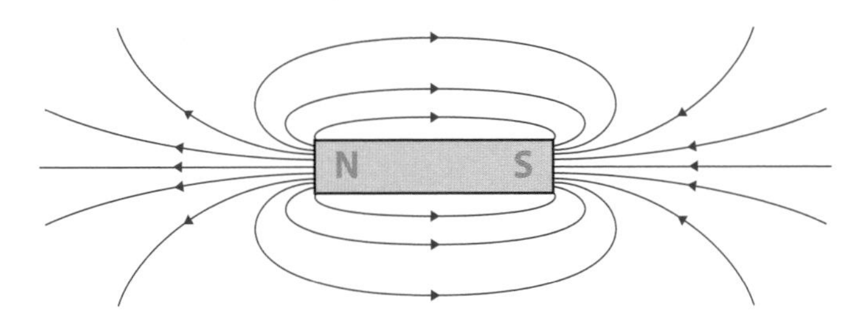

◀ Magnetic field around a bar magnet

A
B
C
D
E
F
G
H
I
J
K
L
M
N
O
P
Q
R
S
T
U
V
W
X
Y
Z

magnetism

This is a natural force, like gravity, which arises from the movement of electrical charge. Magnetic rocks such as magnetite occur naturally. Materials attracted by a *magnet* become magnetised themselves; these magnetic materials include iron, steel, nickel and cobalt.

maintenance

Regular inspection and replacement of worn or damaged parts that will ensure that an electrical installation remains efficient and safe. Large companies usually carry out maintenance during the evenings or holiday periods when machinery, equipment and the electrical installation wiring can be inspected, tested and repaired without loss of business. Maintenance electricians are specialists, covering electronics, safety issues and preventive maintenance, as well as electrical and mechanical repair and installation.

See *Fault diagnosis*

maintenance regulations

Regulation 4 states that all systems, including portable appliances, should be maintained to prevent danger, and records of maintenance and test results should be kept.

marking and labelling

All *fuses* should be labelled to show the size and type. *Circuit breakers* should be labelled to show the nominal *current* rating and details of the circuit they protect. The origin of every installation should be labelled with the date of *periodic inspection and testing*. Unusual *voltages* should be labelled on equipment and enclosures. Earthing and bonding connections should be labelled 'Safety Electrical Connection – Do not remove'.

If an installation includes *residual current devices*, a notice should be posted saying, 'This installation, or part of it, is protected by a device that automatically switches off the supply if an earth fault develops. Test quarterly by pressing the button marked "T" or "Test". The device should switch off the supply and should then be switched on to restore the supply. If the device does not switch off the supply when the button is pressed, seek expert advice.' Mobile caravans must have a notice near the main switch regarding connection and disconnection to site electricity supplies.

▲ Safety electrical connection label

marring

The migration of polymers between PVC-sheathed cables and polystyrene insulation.

mass

The amount of matter in an object or substance. Weight can change, according to gravity, but mass stays the same.

materials list

A document listing the amount of different materials required for a project prepared from a *layout diagram* made to scale. The drawing can be measured and the measurements multiplied according to the scale to work out the amounts of materials required.

maximum demand and diversity

The maximum current demand for a final circuit is the sum of current demands of all the loads with allowance for diversity. (Refer to Appendix 1, Table 1A of the IEE On-Site Guide for typical demands.) A method of assessing the diversity in current use of the various loads is given in Appendix 1, Table 1B, of the IEE On-Site Guide. The sum, with allowance for diversity, is the *assumed current demand*, which is used to determine the rating of a suitable *protective device* and the size of cable.

See *Regulations*

MCB

See *Miniature circuit breaker*

MCCB

See *Moulded case circuit breaker*

mechanical advantage

The relationship between the input and output of a machine, a mechanical advantage exists when less energy is used to do the work. Levers and pulleys are examples of mechanical advantage. The formula for calculating mechanical advantage is:

$$\text{Mechanical Advantage (MA)} = \frac{\text{Load}}{\text{Effort}}$$

MICC cable (mineral-insulated copper cable)

These are high-conductivity copper conductors insulated with compressed *magnesium oxide* and covered with a seamless copper sheath. The cables are fire-resistant, withstanding 1000°C, and are used in emergency lighting and fire-alarm systems. The cable is mechanically strong, ages very well and can carry high currents.

◀ MICC cable

A
B
C
D
E
F
G
H
I
J
K
L
M
N
O
P
Q
R
S
T
U
V
W
X
Y
Z

miniature circuit breaker (MCB)

A switch which opens automatically when excess *current* flows. The switch can be manually closed when the current fault is remedied. The contacts of the circuit breaker are held closed against spring pressure by a latch which will open very quickly in the event of excessive current. The latch may be tripped in two ways:

- Thermal tripping – the MCB has a small heater coil wrapped round a bi metallic strip; when the load current passes through the heater coil the bi metallic strip is warmed; normal currents will not heat the strip enough to make it bend and trip the latch, but an *overcurrent* will.
- Magnetic tripping – a force of attraction is set up by the *magnetic field* of a coil carrying the load current; normally, the magnetic field is not strong enough to attract the latch, but a short circuit current will increase the magnetic field and operate the latch.

Thermal tripping takes longer than magnetic tripping and the two methods are sometimes combined. MCBs are classified according to the current at which they will operate instantaneously. A selection guidance is available in Table 7.2B of the IEE On-Site Guide.

See *Regulations*

Minor Works Certificate (Electrical Installation)

A testing and inspection certificate, including space for test results and used for small projects such as an additional socket outlet or lighting point to an existing circuit. The certificate must identify the persons responsible for design, construction, inspection and testing, and be completed and signed by a competent person with a good understanding of the work and of the technical requirements of BS 7671.

motion detectors

See *Passive infrared sensor (PIR)*

motor control circuits

See *Contactor*

motor speed

The speed of a motor can be expressed as *synchronous speed* or actual speed. Synchronous speed (*a.c. motor*) is the *stator*'s *magnetic field* rotation speed – the rotor turns at a slightly slower rate. The actual speed is the shaft rotation speed – this is the speed given on the nameplate. The difference between the actual and synchronous speeds is the slip, expressed either as a unit or percentage. Synchronous speed (n_s) can be calculated using the following formula:

$$\text{Synchronous speed } (n_s) = \frac{\text{Frequency (f) in Hz}}{\text{The number of pole pairs (p)}}$$

motor starter

A motor starter switches on the supply and automatically disconnects the motor in the event of overloads or other faults. The overload protection may be a solid state electronic device. The starter also prevents automatic restarting (no-volt protection).

▲ Moulded case circuit breaker

motors

See *a.c. motor*; *d.c. motor*; *Induction motor*; *No-volt protection*; *Remote stop/start control*; *Slip-ring motor*; *Synchronous a.c. induction motor*

moulded case circuit breaker (MCCB)

A protective device used for control equipment (switchgear) at the origin of the supply. The manufacturer's instructions should be followed for re-setting tripped MCCBs.

multicore cable

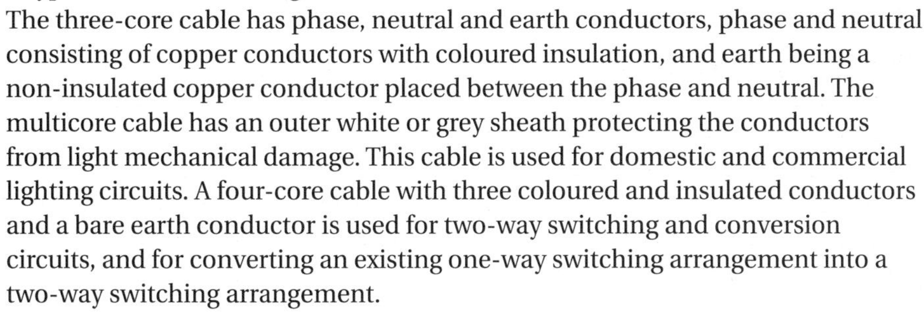

A type of cable containing two or more cables. The three-core cable has phase, neutral and earth conductors, phase and neutral consisting of copper conductors with coloured insulation, and earth being a non-insulated copper conductor placed between the phase and neutral. The multicore cable has an outer white or grey sheath protecting the conductors from light mechanical damage. This cable is used for domestic and commercial lighting circuits. A four-core cable with three coloured and insulated conductors and a bare earth conductor is used for two-way switching and conversion circuits, and for converting an existing one-way switching arrangement into a two-way switching arrangement.

multimeter

An instrument combining the features and characteristics of various test instruments, including an *ammeter* and a *voltmeter*. For example, used for:

- measuring current (ammeter) – this is done by using a series connection (a very low resistance is required)

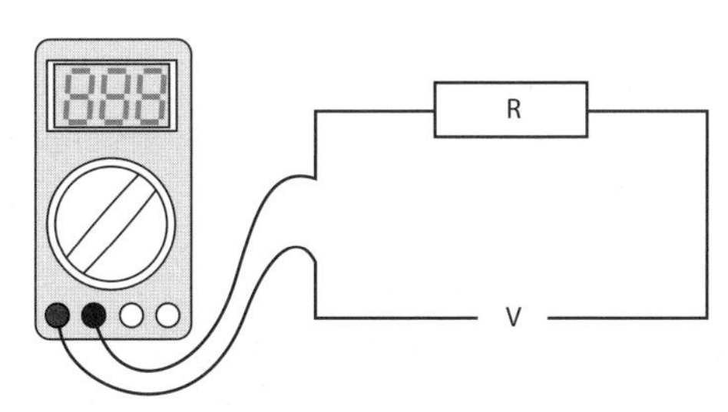

▲ multimeter used as an ammeter to measure current

A B C D E F G H I J K L M N O P Q R S T U V W X Y Z

A B C D E F G H I J K L M N O P Q R S T U V W X Y Z

- measuring voltage (voltmeter) – measuring the potential difference between two points, connected in parallel across the load or circuit to be measured (the internal resistance must be very high).

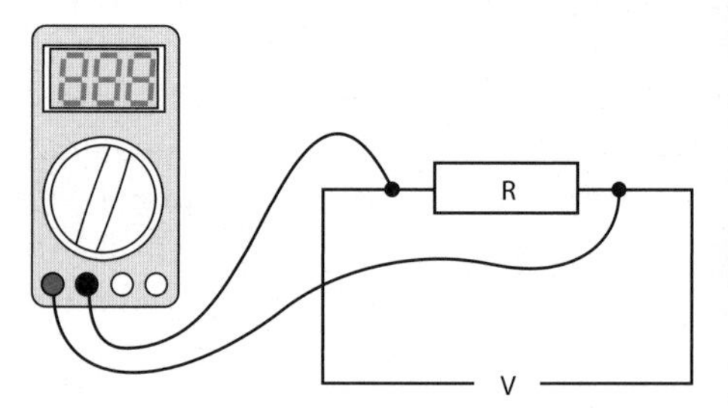

▲ multimeter used as a voltmeter to measure voltage

multiplexer

Multi-input, single output device which, when used in *CCTV* systems, allows the simultaneous recording or viewing of more than one camera image.

mutual detrimental influence – prevention

Electrical services must be protected from services of a different *voltage* band and from non-electrical services. For example, *fire-alarm* and *emergency lighting* circuits must be separated from other types of cable and from each other. Band 1 and Band 2 circuits can only be included in the same enclosure or wiring system if they are segregated or wired with cables suitable for the highest voltage present. Band 1 covers *ELV* circuits (under 50 volts a.c. or 120 volts d.c.); Band 2 covers low voltage (under 1000 volts between conductors or 600 volts to earth).

mutual inductance

An *electromotive force* produced in one circuit by a change in the *current* flowing in an adjacent circuit. *Transformers* use mutual inductance in their operation.

See *Inductance*

national grid

A network of power lines linking power generating facilities across the country. This system ensures that electricity remains available when a generating facility is not operating. Electricity is mainly transmitted through steel-cored aluminium conductors suspended from steel pylons. The grid supply is taken off and transformed down to 11 kV at special stations then distributed to local sub stations where it is transformed again down to 400 V. The electricity is then supplied to the customer, mainly through underground circuits.

National Inspection Council for Electrical Installation Contracting (NICEIC)

An independent electrical safety regulatory body.

neozed fuse

A fuse developed to European testing regulations and approved by all European testing authorities. This fuse now replaces the type 'D' fuse.

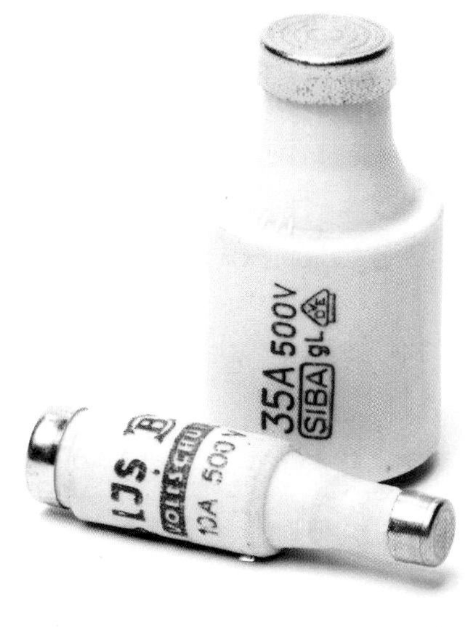

◀ Neozed fuses

A B C D E F G H I J K L M N O P Q R S T U V W X Y Z

network

A system of linked computers connected with structured cable installation.

neutrons

Electrically neutral particles found in the nucleus of an atom.

newton

The force required to accelerate an object weighing one kilogram at a rate of one metre per second per second.

noggin

A small piece of wood placed between joists or wall studwork so that fixtures may be attached.

non-fused spurs

A radial branch connected to a ring circuit at the terminal of a socket outlet, at a junction box or at the origin of the circuit in the distribution board. Each non-fused spur can supply one single or one twin-socket outlet, or one item of permanently connected equipment. The number of non-fused spurs connected to a ring circuit must not exceed the sum of socket outlets and items of fixed equipment directly connected. The conductor for a non-fused spur must be the same size as the conductor on the ring circuit.

See *Spur*

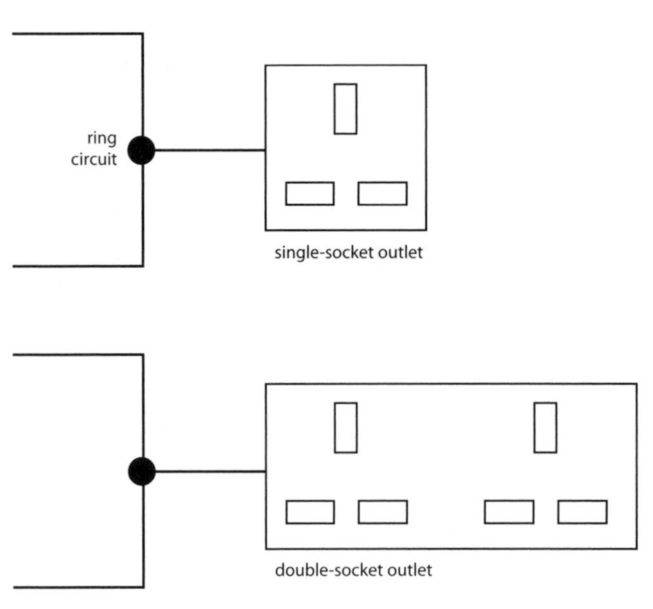

▲ Non-fused spurs

non-live tests

These are performed before the wiring circuit is energised. They are part of the wiring regulations, BS 7671 Part 7. The tests include: the continuity of protective conductors; the continuity of the ring final circuit conductors; insulation resistance; polarity.

non-pressure water heater

An instantaneous water heater usually rated at less than 3 kW and holding less than 15 litres of water.

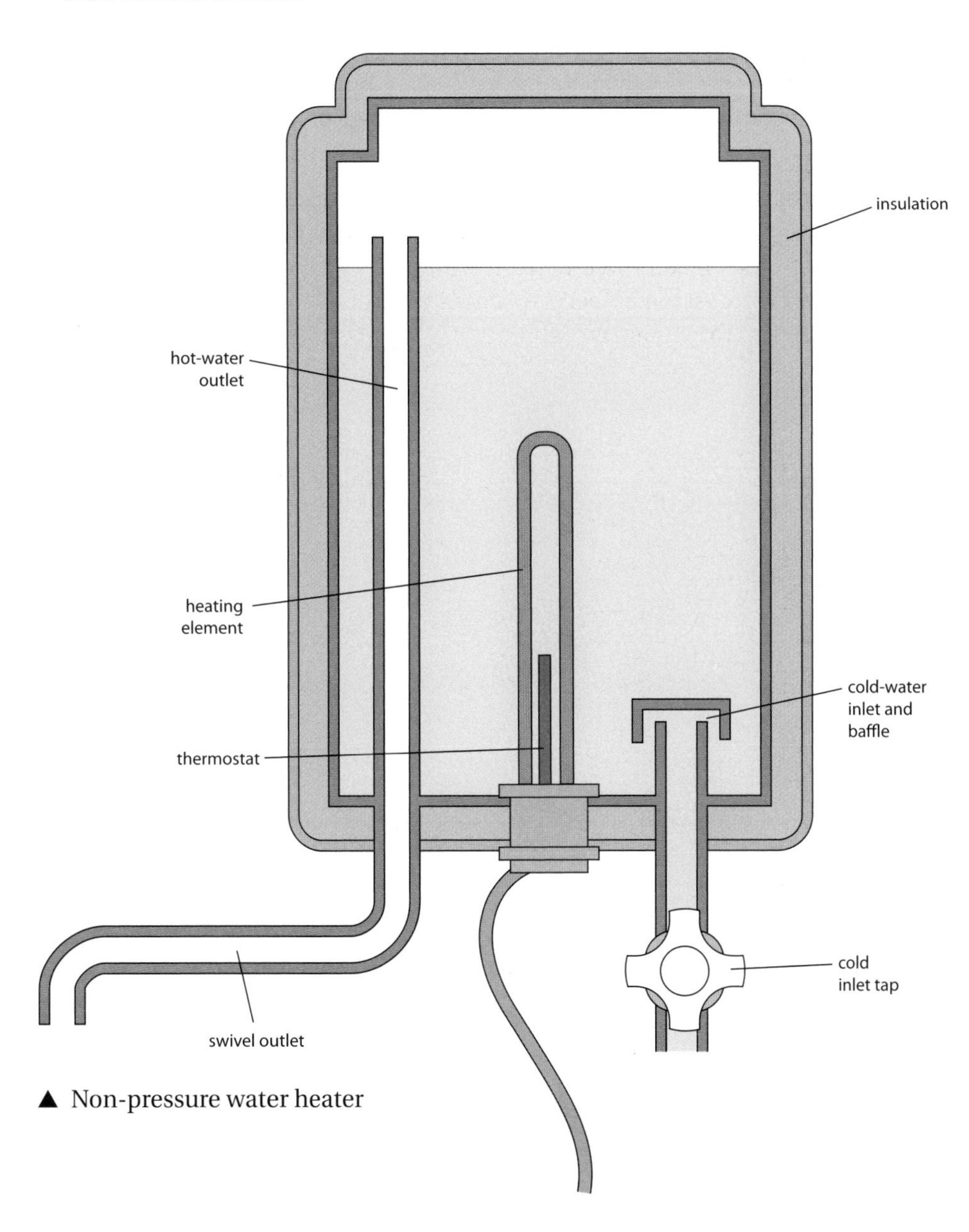

▲ Non-pressure water heater

A
B
C
D
E
F
G
H
I
J
K
L
M
N
O
P
Q
R
S
T
U
V
W
X
Y
Z

normally closed (n/c)

A set of contacts that are normally in the closed position, and open when energised.

normally open (n/o)

A set of contacts that are normally in the open position, and close when energised.

no-volt protection

A safety device installed within a motor, designed to prevent the motor restarting after an unexpected loss of voltage. Otherwise a machine may unexpectedly restart when voltage is restored which is hazardous. In such cases, regulations require that a motor starter, including a *contactor* is provided, which will prevent automatic restarting. This is also called under voltage protection.

nucleus

The centre of an atom which contains *protons* and *neutrons*.

O

off-load devices

See *On- and off-load devices*

ohmmeter

An analogue or digital instrument used to measure *resistance*. The meter operates on a battery, and the *current* which flows through the meter is dependent on the value of the resistance being measured. After turning the supply off, both leads of the meter are connected and the variable resistor is adjusted to zero (full-scale deflection). *Insulation resistance* ohmmeters must be capable of measuring high resistance.

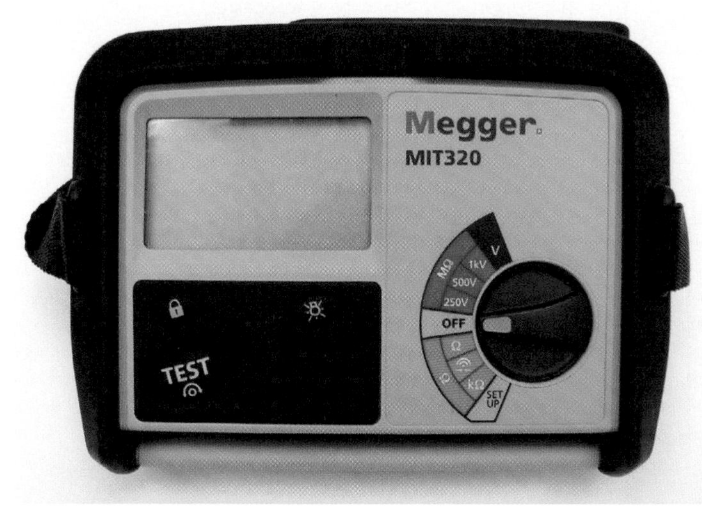

▲ Modern insulation and continuity tester

Ohm's Law

The German physicist G. S. Ohm discovered that, at a constant temperature, the current flowing in a circuit is directly proportional to the voltage. So, the voltage (V) is equal to the current (I) multiplied by the resistance (R). Ohm's law can be expressed by the following formula:

$$V = IR$$

Ohm's Law may also be written as:

$$I = \frac{V}{R}$$

or as:

$$R = \frac{V}{I}$$

See *Current*; *Resistance*; *Voltage*

oil dashpot

A type of *solenoid* used in *circuit breakers* to produce time-delay tripping. The time lag can be adjusted by altering the size of the oil-escape hole in the dashpot.

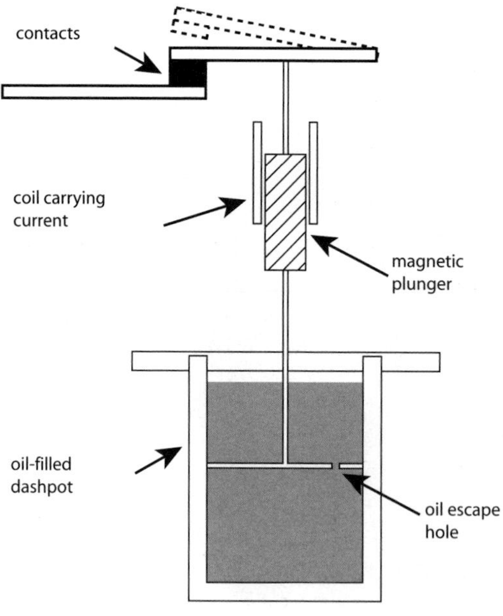

▲ Oil-filled dashpot

oil-filled radiator

A heating appliance filled with oil and containing heating elements cased in pressed steel. Oil heats up and cools down faster than water as it has a lower specific heat capacity. It is used for direct heating.

olive

A metal ring tightened under a threaded nut to form a seal on the sheath of mineral insulated (*MICC*) cable. It is also known as a compression ring.

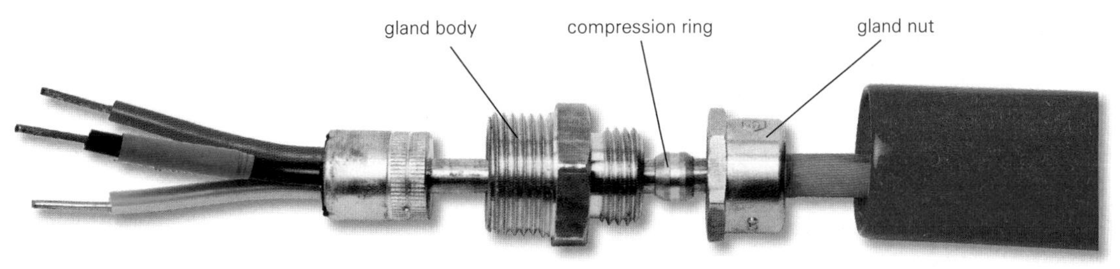

▲ MICC gland showing olive (compression ring)

on- and off-load devices

When a switch or disconnector is used to break a circuit with a *current* flowing through it, the current arcs as it dissipates and makes contact across the switch terminals, sometimes causing a brief flash of light. This also happens when circuits are switched off or when *protective devices* break *fault current* levels. An on-load device can be operated when current is flowing, for example a *circuit breaker*, which can make and break load current and withstand high levels of fault current. An off-load device is an *isolator* designed to operate when there is no load current to break.

one-way switch

A normal domestic light switch is an example of a one-way switch. Pressing the switch to the on position closes the internal switch contact which is mechanically held in place across the terminals. When the pressure is removed the switch remains in position and the light stays on.

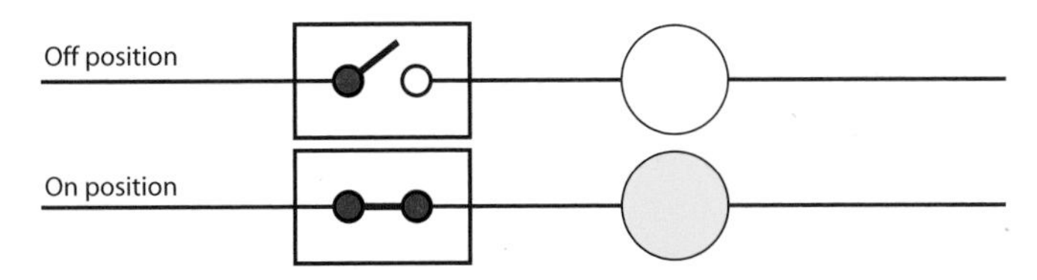

▲ One-way switch

A
B
C
D
E
F
G
H
I
J
K
L
M
N
O
P
Q
R
S
T
U
V
W
X
Y
Z

open area (anti-panic) lighting

A form of *emergency lighting* provided in and around public buildings to illuminate escape routes and exits. All emergency lighting must be installed in accordance with the *British Standard* specification (BS 5266 Part 1: 1999 – Code of Practice for Emergency Lighting).

operating devices

Used to provide switching and isolation of circuits or complete installations having one or more of the following functions: control, isolation or protection. When a circuit or an electrical appliance is isolated prior to starting work, it is essential to ensure that it cannot be switched back on accidentally. This may be achieved by locking off the device with a padlock.

▲ Device locked off with padlock

opto-coupler

A *light emitting diode (LED)* with a *photodiode* or phototransistor which transfers analogue or digital signals from one circuit to another. The opto-coupler is used when the circuits cannot be electrically connected, for example when the *voltages* are different in the two circuits. The opto-coupler is also known as an opto-isolator.

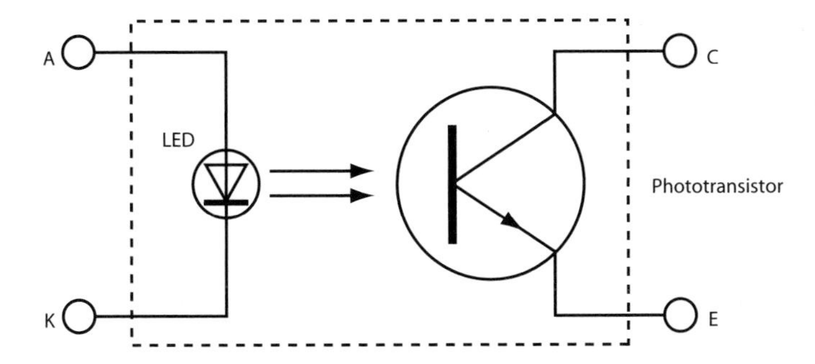

▲ Opto-coupler circuit

out of phase

This occurs when the *current* and *voltage* alternate at different times, and are said to be out of phase with each other.

See *In phase*

out-of-reach protection

One method of protection against electric shock, by placing live electrical parts out of reach. The requirements for this method of protection are described in the Memorandum of Guidance to the Electricity at Work *Regulations* 1989.

oven thermostat

The two main types of oven thermostat are the capillary type and the stem type. The capillary type has an 800 mm tube filled with liquid which expands when heated. The liquid presses a capsule in the control housing, which pushes the plunger in the pressure block and opens the contacts. The oven heating elements are then switched off. The stem type varies in length and has a copper tube with an Invar rod inside. When heated, the copper expands faster than the Invar and pushes against the rod which opens the contacts. (See diagrams overleaf.)

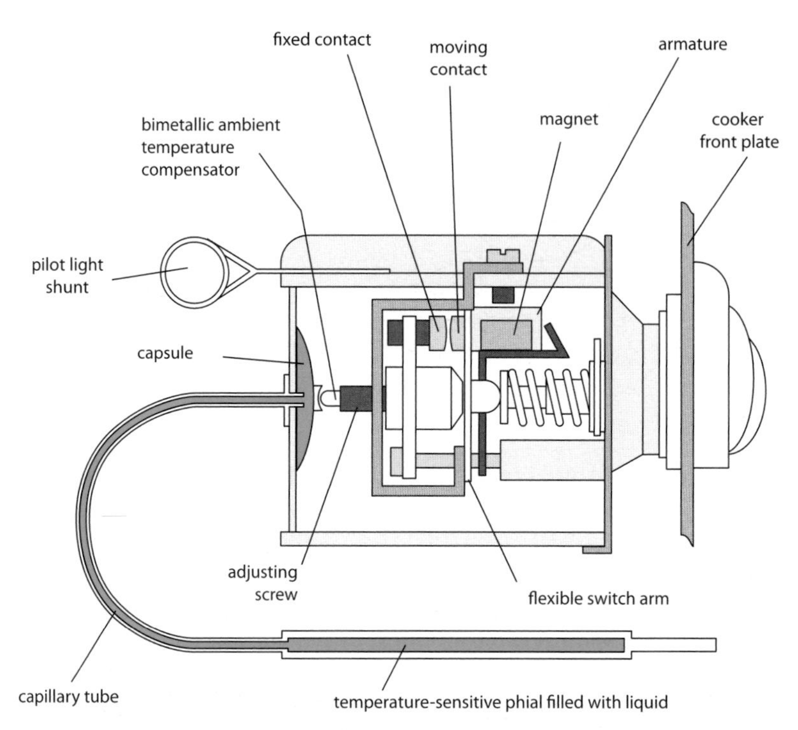

▲ Capillary type oven thermostat

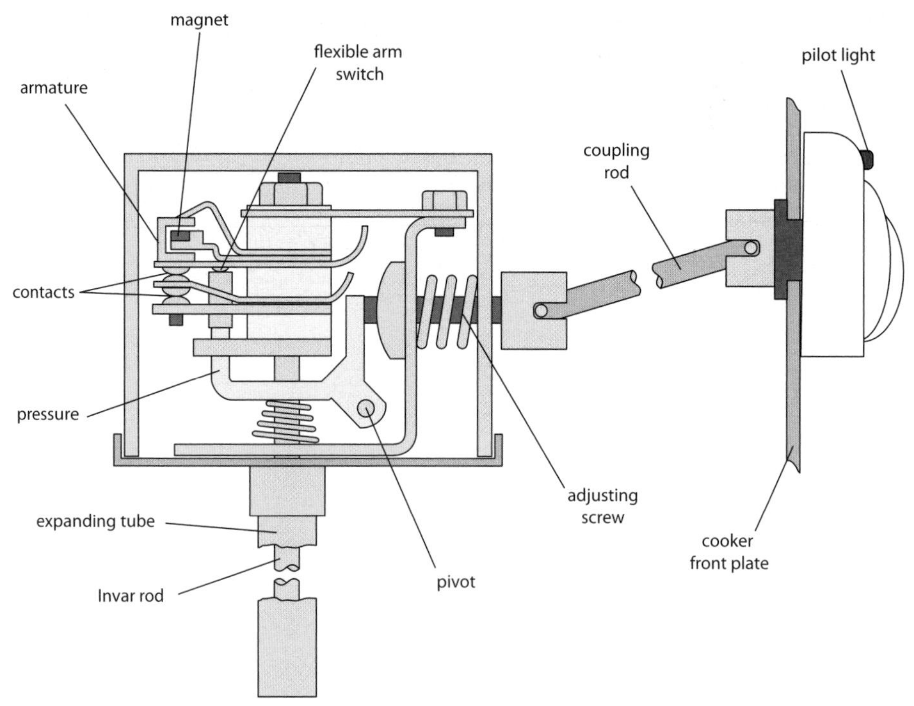

▲ Stem type oven thermostat

overcurrent

Current that exceeds the rated value or carrying capacity of a *conductor*. The overcurrent may not be a circuit fault. Short-term overloads specific to a piece of equipment or outlet may also occur.

overcurrent protection

Protective devices such as *circuit breakers* or *fuses*, designed to operate when more *current* passes through a circuit than the circuit is designed to take. The devices operate within a specific time and disconnect the supply automatically in the event of an overload, short circuits or earth faults. The excess current creates heat which will rupture a fuse element or trip a circuit breaker. Overcurrent protection devices include:

- rewirable fuses (*BS 3036*)
- cartridge fuses (*BS 1361/BS 1362*)
- HRC fuses (*BS 88 HBC fuses*)
- type 'D' and *neozed fuses*
- *miniature circuit breakers* (BS EN 60898 or BS 3871 MCBs).

The level of protection required for radial circuits are listed in the table below.

Type of circuit	Overcurrent protection device		Type of protective device		Maximum floor area served
1	2 Rating A	3 Rating A	4 (PVC) mm^2	5 (MICC) mm^2	6 m^2
A1 Ring	30 or 32	Any	2.5	1.5	100
A2 Radial	30 or 32	Cartridge fuse or circuit breaker	4	2.5	75
A3 Radial	20	Any	2.5	1.5	50

▲ Overcurrent protection

A
B
C
D
E
F
G
H
I
J
K
L
M
N
O
P
Q
R
S
T
U
V
W
X
Y
Z

overhead power lines

An above ground method of distributing electrical energy around the country from where it is generated to where it is needed. Overhead power lines may have voltages as high as 400 kV to reduce transmission currents. This means smaller, lighter cables can be used and switchgear can have a lower current rating and be cheaper. Insulation is generally not used at the higher voltages as it enables the cables to run cooler.

More than 50 per cent of fatal electrical accidents each year are caused by contact with overhead power lines. If work is being done near overhead lines, it may be possible to have them switched off; if this is not possible, it is vital to conform to the safe working distance.

overload current

Overcurrent which occurs in an electrically sound circuit, for example: exceeding the rated load of a circuit by using adaptors in socket outlets; adding extra load to an existing circuit; not accounting for starting current on a motor circuit.

oxidation

A chemical reaction which combines a substance with oxygen. Rust is the product of the oxidation of iron.

panel building

The control of the distribution of electricity and of electrical systems and equipment is achieved through panels. These are usually manufactured in an electrical products factory, but some control panel products are constructed on site. The three types of panel manufactured are *switchgear*, *control panels* and *motor control circuits*.

parallel circuits

When *resistors* are connected in a way that allows *current* to flow by two or more different routes, then the circuit is said to be parallel. In a parallel circuit the current divides to flow along different branches of the circuit. The voltage will be the same across each of the branches and disconnection of one branch will not affect the others.

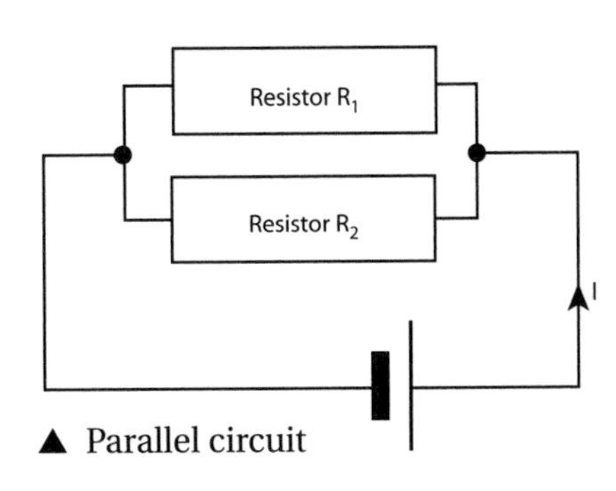

▲ Parallel circuit

parallel earth paths

Two or more routes that an earth fault can follow back to the supply transformer start point. Parallel earth paths can lower Z_s values but can give false Z_e values.

passive infrared (PIR) sensor

A type of motion detector used in surveillance and security systems. The PIR sensor uses ceramic infrared detectors and detects the infrared heat radiated from the human body.

PAT (portable appliance testing)

The Electricity at Work Regulations 1989 (EAWR) require that tools powered by 110 volts or 230 volts be tested regularly. Regular visual inspection is not adequate and a testing programme should be implemented using approved

A B C D E F G H I J K L M N O P Q R S T U V W X Y Z

test instruments. The PAT test will detect all faults such as damaged flex or exposed live parts. Records should be kept to ensure testing is carried out with adequate frequency. The Institution of Engineering & Technology (formerly the IEE) suggests that portable equipment is tested before use and every six months thereafter. Visual inspections should be conducted monthly for Class I equipment and every three months for Class II.

pattress

A plastic plate or box fixed to the wall or ceiling surface so that an electric light switch or socket outlet can be fitted.

peak value

The maximum value of either positive or negative *a.c.* or *d.c.* waveforms.

PELV (protective extra low voltage)

See *ELV (extra low voltage)*

PEN

Protective earth neutral, often found on *TN-C-S earthing systems*.

perimeter protection

Electrical devices used to detect intruders before they break into a premises. Perimeter protection includes *proximity switches* and *inertia switches*, both of which will detect movement or intrusion and send a signal to the alarm panel which activates the sounder.

periodic inspection and testing

It is essential to conduct periodic inspection and testing as the condition of electrical installations deteriorates over time owing to wear and tear, accidental damage and corrosion. The Electricity at Work Regulations 1989 require that systems are maintained to prevent danger, as far as is reasonably practicable. Licensing authorities, insurance companies and mortgage lenders may also require inspection and testing to be carried out on a regular basis. The 16th edition of the IEE Wiring *Regulations* became a *British Standard* BS 7671; Part 7 deals with inspection and testing. The frequency of periodic inspection and testing depends on the type of installation. The visual inspection includes the identification of conductors, routing of cables, connection of conductors etc. A periodic inspection report should be completed when conducting a periodic inspection and test of an existing installation. The requirements for the content and completion of documentation are covered in the introduction to Appendix 6 of BS 7671.

permanent magnet

Material that develops and retains a *magnetic field* after insertion in a strong magnetic field. The material then attracts or repels other magnetic materials. The magnetic field from a permanent magnet arises from the spin and orbital motion of electrons. The amount of magnetisation retained is called its *remanence*. The amount of reverse driving field required to demagnetise it is called *coercivity*.

permanent split capacitor (PSC) motor

A *capacitor* motor without a starting switch or starting capacitor. In the PSC motor, a run-type capacitor is connected in series permanently with the start winding. The second winding is permanently connected to the power source. The start winding becomes an auxiliary winding when the motor reaches running speed. The run capacitor cannot provide the starting boost of a starting capacitor, therefore starting *torque* is low, from 30 to 150 per cent of rated load. PSC motors have low starting currents, usually less than 200 per cent of rated load current.

permanently connected equipment

This type of equipment must either have a local fuse (maximum 13 A) and a switch control complying with BS 7671, or have circuit breaker protection (maximum 16 A).

Permit to Work

A document that specifies the details of work to be done, when it is going to be done, the hazards involved and the precautions to be taken, and it authorises the people to be involved in the work. Electricians are often involved in potentially dangerous work and the Permit to Work system provides safeguards in these cases. A permit for work is active for a set period and must be returned to the authorising person when the work is complete. The authorising person must be competent and understand completely the work to be done, the hazards, the proposed system of work, the precautions needed and the level of skills required to perform the work. If the people authorised to do the work have not returned the permit by the allocated time, an investigation will proceed immediately. Separate permit forms may be used for hot work and entry into confined spaces, emphasising the particular hazards and precautions required.

petrol filling stations

A facility which sells fuel and lubricants for motor vehicles. Strict guidelines must be followed when carrying out electrical installations in these areas because of the risk of an electric spark igniting gas vapour.

Standards and guidelines for electrical installations in petrol filling stations are covered by BS EN 60079, Parts 10, 14 and 17, and the electrical section of the Institute of Petroleum and the Association for Petroleum and Explosives Administration (IP/APEA) publication, 'Guidance for the Design, Construction, Modification and Maintenance of Petrol Filling Stations'.

phase

The correct term for any live conductor.

See *In phase*; *Out of phase*

A B C D E F G H I J K L M N O P Q R S T U V W X Y Z

A
B
C
D
E
F
G
H
I
J
K
L
M
N
O
P
Q
R
S
T
U
V
W
X
Y
Z

phase angle

The difference in degrees between the *voltage* and the *current* in an *a.c.* circuit. See *Cosine*; *Phasor diagrams*; *Power factor*

▲ Phasor diagram for zero phase angle

phase current

The current flowing through any one component in a three-phase source or load.

phase voltage

The voltage measured across a single component in a three-phase source or load.

phasor

A representation of the magnitude of, and the phase relationship between, *voltage* and *current* in a circuit. The length of the line is proportional to the magnitude of both current and voltage, and the angle between them shows whether the circuit is lagging or leading. The current will lag the voltage in an *inductive circuit* whereas it will lead the voltage in a *capacitive circuit*, as seen in the following diagrams:

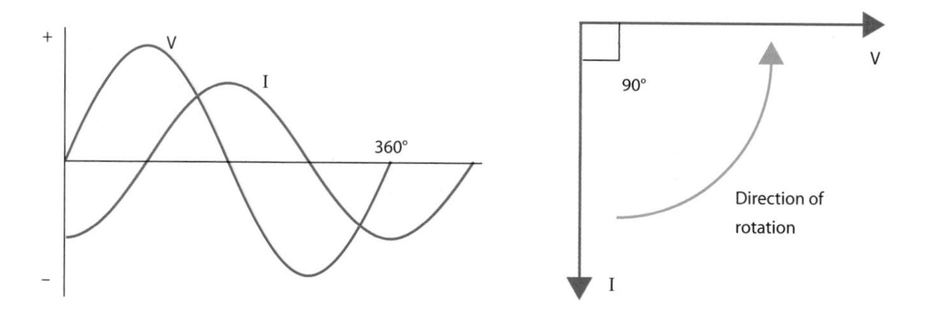

▲ Sine waves and phasor diagrams for inductive circuits

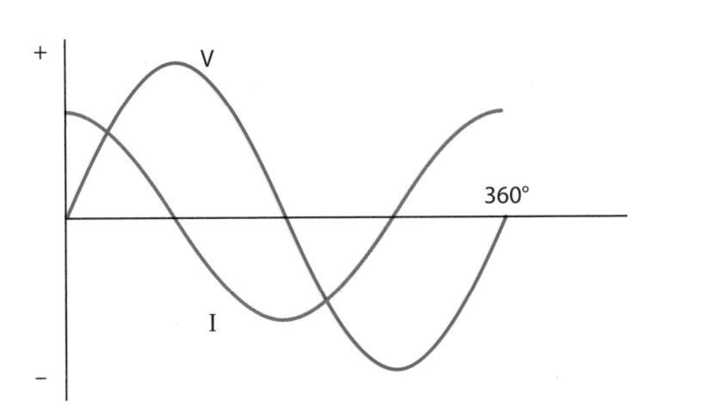

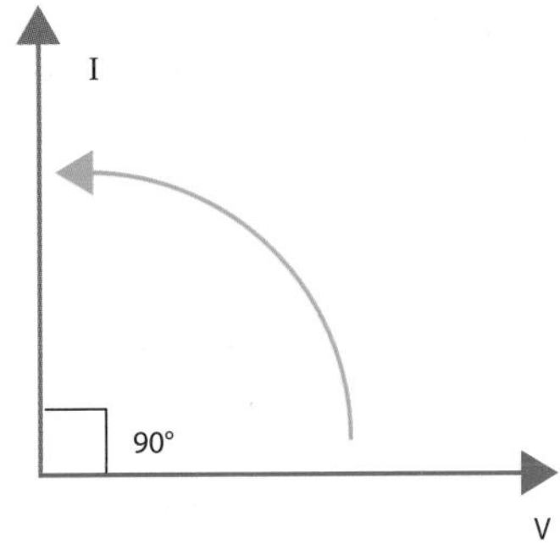

▲ Sine waves and phasor diagrams for capacitive circuits

The angle between the voltage and the current is termed the phase angle. The diagrams show a 90° phase angle which assumes that there is no *resistance* in the circuit. In practice, as there is always some resistance in the circuit, the phase angle will be less than 90°.

phasor diagram

A diagram representing an alternating quantity (*voltage* or *current*) where the magnitude of the quantities are proportional to the length of the lines. The relationship of the quantities is shown by the angle between the voltage and the current and is termed the *phase angle*.

When sine waves for voltage and current are not in phase, phasor diagrams are used. A quantity that has the same value at all parts of the circuit is chosen as the reference phasor and is drawn horizontally. In a series circuit the same current flows in each part of the circuit, so the current is used as the reference phasor. In a parallel circuit, the voltage is used as the reference phasor.

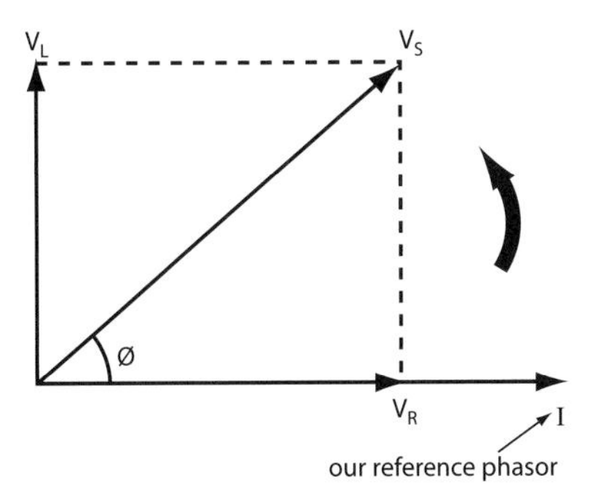

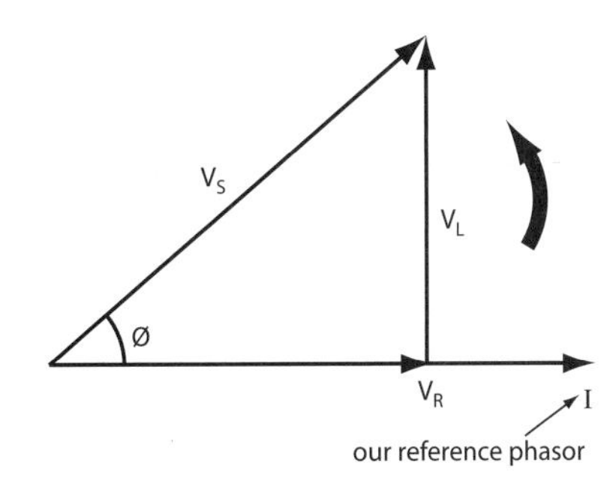

▲ Two ways of drawing a phasor diagram

phenol-formaldehyde insulation

A thermosetting polymer which can withstand temperatures over 100°C and is used to manufacture socket outlets, plug tops, switches and consumer units.

photocell

A photocell can change visible light, infrared and ultraviolet radiation into electrical signals. They are used in burglar and fire alarms and counting and automatic control systems. The photocell uses *semiconductors* whose *resistance* decreases with the increase in intensity of light.

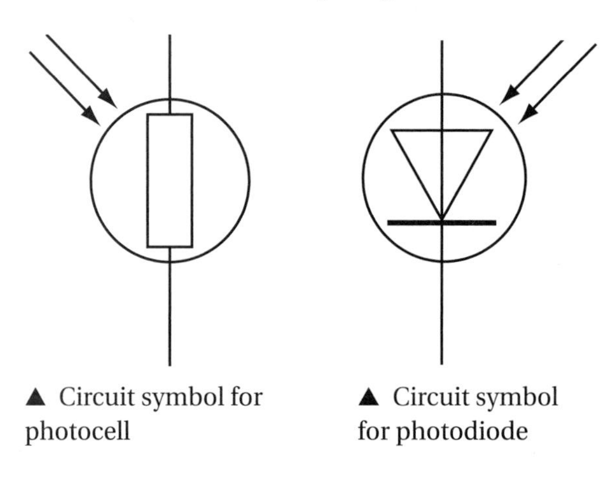

▲ Circuit symbol for photocell

▲ Circuit symbol for photodiode

photodiode

A *p-n junction* which responds to optical input through a window or optical fibre connection. Photodiodes can be used in zero or reverse bias. Reverse-biased diodes have very high *resistance* which is reduced when light shines on the junction. The light energy breaks the bonds in the structure of the semiconductor material producing electrons and allowing current to flow. The reverse-biased photodiode is used to measure light intensity.

Solar cells operate on the photovoltaic effect of zero-biased photodiodes. Light falling on the diode develops a *voltage* across the device and causes *current* in the forward bias direction. The solar cell can power equipment such as calculators, solar panels and satellites orbiting the earth.

PILCSWA cables

Paper insulated, lead covered, steel wired, armoured cables that are used on systems at 3.3 kV and over. Special training is required before an electrician can work on this type of cable.

pillar terminal

A terminal comprising a brass pillar with a hole through its side. The conductor cable is inserted into the hole and secured with a setscrew. If the conductor cable is too small for the hole, double the cable over before inserting it into the hole. If more than one conductor has to be secured in the same terminal, they should be twisted together.

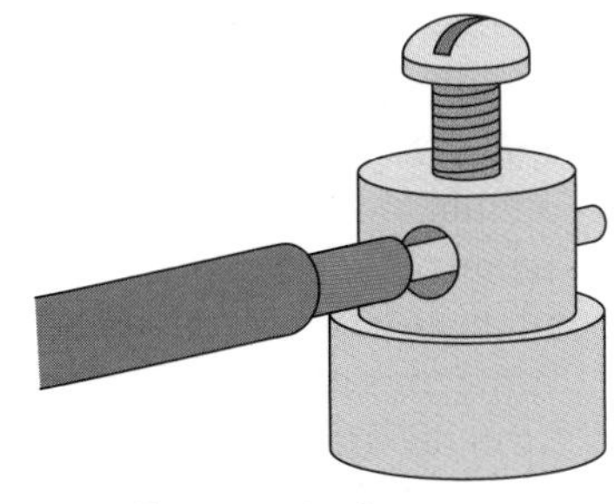

▲ Pillar terminal

plastic connector

A connector used for connecting two cables to make a sound (good) joint. They are commonly called 'chocolate blocks'. They are one of the most common types of connector and are available in 5 A, 15 A, 20 A, 30 A and 50 A ratings. The size required relates to the *current* rating of the circuit.

pliers and cutters

Electricians' pliers have insulated handles and either flat serrated jaws for gripping and bending, or oval serrated jaws for gripping pipes and other cylindrical objects.

PME (protective multiple earthing)

The most common earthing system used. The incoming supply neutral is used as the earth point. Circuit protective conductors connect all installation metal work to the earth terminal. All phase-to-earth faults are then converted to phase-to-neutral faults. This means that under fault conditions a heavier current will flow, and the *protective devices* will operate faster. The increase in *fault current* could cause two hazards: a greater fire risk and a shock risk which could extend to all the protected metalwork on installations connected to the supply distribution network. Conditions for the use of PME systems include: the neutral conductor is earthed at a number of points along its length; there must be no *fuse* or link that could break the neutral path; the main equipotential bonding conductor should be selected in accordance with the neutral conductor of the supply and Table 54H of BS 7671.

See *TN-C*; *TN-C-S*; *TN-S*; *TT*

p-n junction

The junction within a semi-conductor device such as a *diode*, *transistor* or *thyristor*, which allows *current* to flow easily in one direction but not the other.

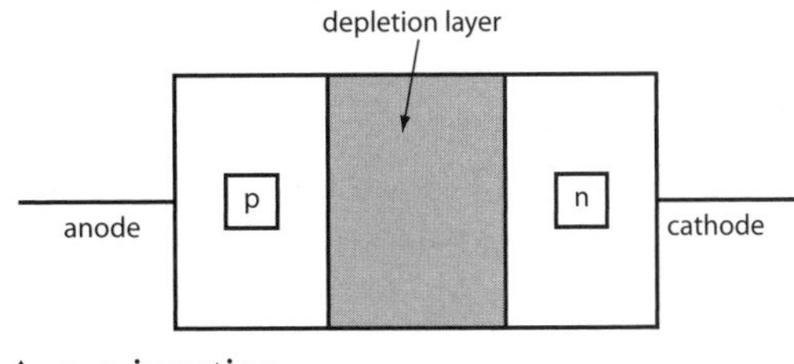

▲ p-n junction

A semiconductor diode is formed when 'n-type' material, with an extra electron per atom, and 'p-type', with one electron removed, are brought together to form a p-n junction. A barrier, called a depletion layer, is formed where the two materials meet. The diode allows current to flow in one direction only.

A B C D E F G H I J K L M N O P Q R S T U V W X Y Z

polarity testing

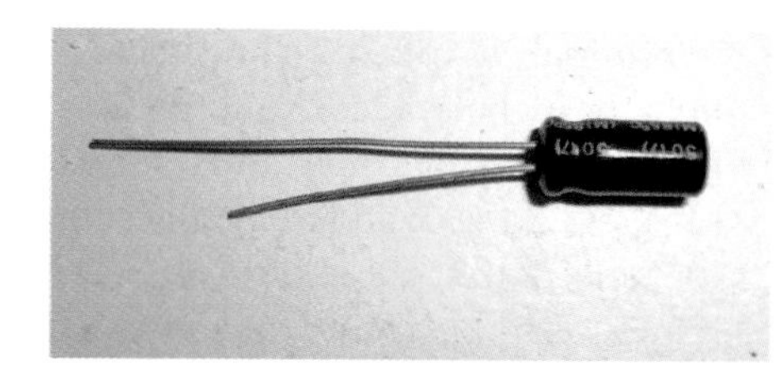

▲ Capacitor showing polarity

In order to meet the requirements of BS 7671, periodic testing of equipment should include verification of the polarity of all circuits. The purpose of the test is to ascertain that all protective devices and single-pole switches are connected to the phase conductor and that the phase terminal in socket outlets and the centre contact of screw-type lamp holders are also connected to the phase conductor. The test must be done before connection to the supply, with either an *ohmmeter* or the continuity range of an insulation and continuity tester.

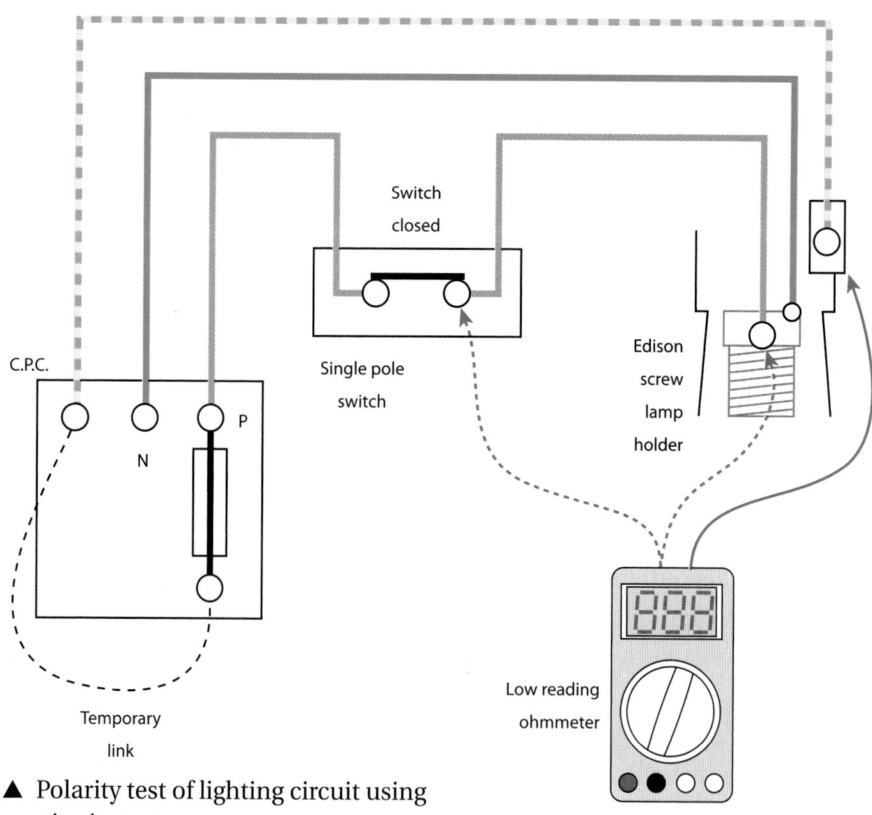

▲ Polarity test of lighting circuit using continuity tester

Polarity is either correct or incorrect. Correct polarity is achieved by the correct termination of conductors to the terminals. Incorrect polarity is caused by the termination of live conductors to the wrong terminals. The polarity of the incoming supply should also be checked to ensure that it is correct. If it is incorrect, then the whole installation would have the wrong polarity.

pole pair

Every magnet has a north and south pole; this is called a pole pair.

porcelain connector

Connector used in high temperature conditions, such as in water heaters, space heaters and luminaires.

portable appliance testing

See *PAT*

pot fitting and sealing

A method for terminating mineral-insulated copper cables (*MICC*). MICCs have copper conductors insulated by compressed *magnesium oxide* powder and covered with a copper sheath. If MICCs are not sealed at both ends, the magnesium oxide insulator will absorb moisture. The seal is formed using a brass pot filled with gland body compound; the pot has a disc to close the mouth and sleeves to insulate the conductor tails.

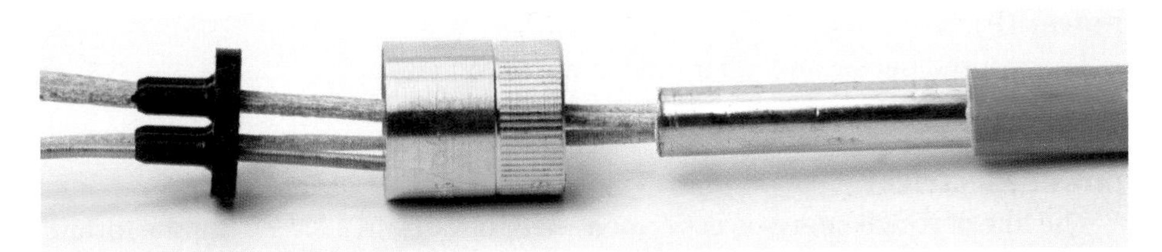

▲ MICC pot and seal

potential difference

The energy used by one coulomb as it passes between two points in a circuit. The potential difference is measured in volts. The reference point that potential is measured against is the earth, which is taken as zero potential or 0 V. A voltage of 230 V means a potential of 230 V above zero.

potential energy

All objects have stored energy, which means that they have the potential to cause change. Potential energy due to height is called gravitational potential energy.

A
B
C
D
E
F
G
H
I
J
K
L
M
N
O
P
Q
R
S
T
U
V
W
X
Y
Z

potentiometer

A device which produces a variable *voltage* supply. A circuit often requires different voltages at different stages; this is achieved using a potentiometer, sometimes called a 'pot'. The potentiometer is a variable resistor and is connected as shown in the diagram. The potentiometer resistor is a track, one ends forms the V+ connection, and the other end forms the 0V connection. The output voltage (Vo) is produced through a movable contact or wiper which can make contact with the track at any point.

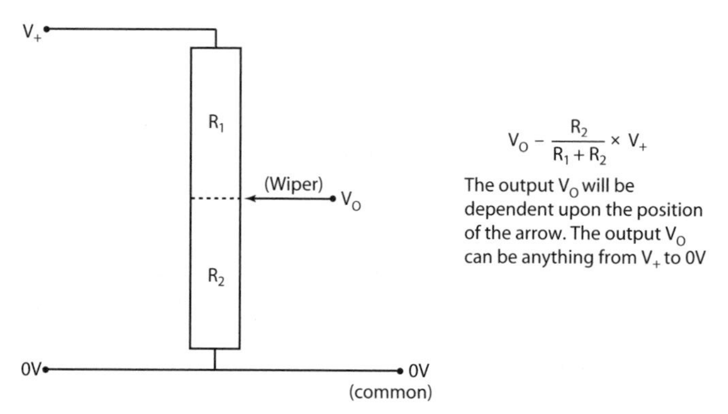

▲ Circuit diagram for voltage applied across a potentiometer

power (P)

Energy used per second, measured in watts (W).

See *Power factor*; *Reactive power*

power, electrical

The rate at which energy is used, measured in watts. In a *d.c.* circuit the formula for calculating the power used in watts is:

$$P = V \times I$$

In an *a.c.* circuit a different formula is used because components such as *capacitors* and *inductors* will cause the *current* to lag or lead the voltage. For a single-phase a.c. circuit the following formula is used:

$$P = V \times I \times \cos \emptyset$$

power factor

The ratio of *apparent* to *true power* in a circuit. The power factor is a number of 1 (unity) or less than 1.0 and is calculated using the following formula:

$$PF = \frac{PT}{PA}$$

or:

$$PF = \frac{W}{VI}$$

Where:
PT = True Power
PA = Apparent Power
W = Power
V = Voltage
I = Current

power factor correction

The smaller the *power factor* (i.e. the larger the *phase angle*), the higher the current has to be for a given amount of true power. This is worse with a highly *inductive circuit*. The power factor can be corrected by inserting a large *capacitor* across the load.

pre-commissioning tests

Commissioning involves a full inspection of the installation and completion of all tests required. The tests conducted before the installation is started up are called pre-commissioning tests. Commissioning tests are conducted when the power is available.

probe

An instrument used for testing circuits, also called a test probe. Quality probes and leads will have finger barriers or be shaped to guard against inadvertent

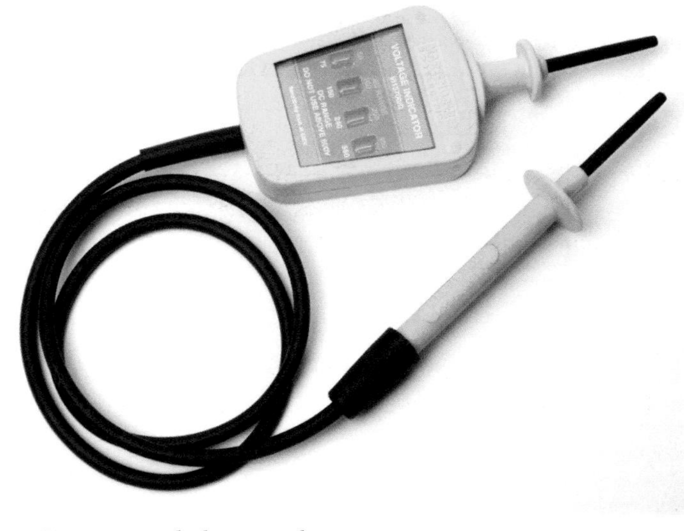

▲ Recommended test probe

A B C D E F G H I J K L M N O P Q R S T U V W X Y Z

hand contact with the live *conductors* under test. They should also be insulated leaving less than 2 mm of exposed metal tip, preferably less than 1 mm. Spring-loaded retractable-screened probes are available, which are safer. All probes should have a high breaking capacity *fuse* with a current rating less than 500 mA, or a current limiting *resistor* and a fuse.

programmer

The most common programmer is used to switch on heating and hot water in domestic properties. This type of programmer is mains operated and has a rechargeable battery which maintains settings for up to two days if there is a power failure. The programmer may be set to switch heating or hot water, or both services, on and off at several different times during the day. The supply to the programmer, and the rest of the circuit, is usually through a *fused spur* with a 3 A fuse.

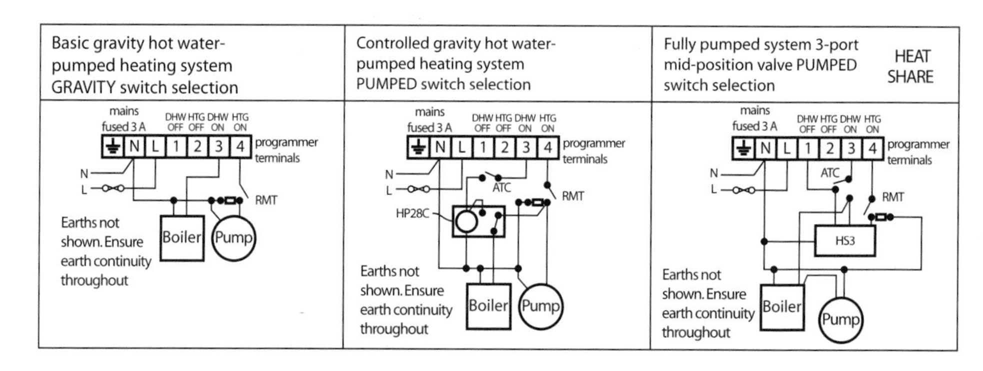

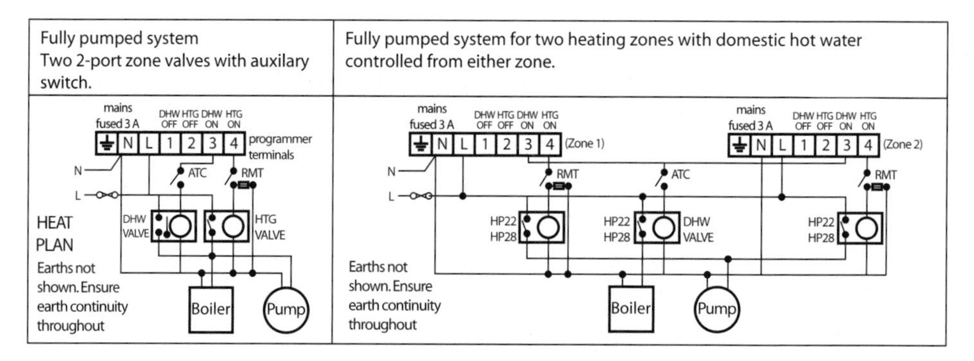

▲ Wiring diagram for timer and programming domestic system

prospective short-circuit current (PSSC)

The prospective *fault current* must be considered when selecting *overcurrent* devices. Short-circuit current may cause: a thermal effect, which could melt *conductors* and *insulation*, cause fire and alter the properties of materials; a mechanical effect, in which large *magnetic fields* may build up when short-circuit currents flow and this could cause conductor distortion and breakage of supports and insulators. Rapid disconnection of the supply is essential.

protective conductor – continuity

Protective conductors are installed in final circuit wiring and in wiring from the main earthing terminals to the metalwork in the installation. The *continuity* of protective conductors must be verified as they are an essential safety device if an earth fault arises and will ensure the operation of protective devices and fuses. A low resistance value on conductors is verified using a low-resistance *ohmmeter*. The test current for testing the continuity of equipotential bonding should be at least 200 mA. The earth continuity reading should be between 0.01 and 0.05 ohms.

protective device

A device which stop the supply of power to a faulty device, or circuit. If a fault occurs, it must be investigated and corrected before switching the device on again. Protective devices must be set correctly for the load. The rating of a protective device should be equal to, or greater than, the rating of the circuit or equipment protected.

proton

Positively charged particle in the nucleus of an atom.

proximity switch

A *perimeter protection* device which detects the opening of a door or window. The device has two parts, a magnet and a reed switch, fixed side by side less than 6 mm apart on a door or window. When the door or window opens the magnet stops holding the reed switch closed and the opening of the switch activates the alarm.

purchase order

A document sent to a supplier specifying details of material and quantity required, the manufacturer and the required delivery date and place.

PUWER (Provision and Use of Work Equipment Regulations 1998)

These *regulations* require the prevention and control of risks to Health and Safety from equipment used at work. Equipment provided for work must be suitable for the job, safe to use, well-maintained and inspected, used by suitably trained people and provided with all suitable safety measures. The equipment covered by this legislation includes hand tools, power tools, ladders, scaffolds, electronic equipment and motor vehicles. Employees providing their own equipment are also required to comply with the regulations.

A B C D E F G H I J K L M N O P Q R S T U V W X Y Z

PVC cable

Cable insulated with polyvinyl chloride (PVC) which is a thermoplastic polymer. These cables are economic and used widely for lighting and power installations in domestic properties. PVC cable should only be used in temperatures between 0 and 60°C (BS 7671) and mechanical protection against damage may be required. Single-core PVC-insulated unsheathed cable (6491X) is used for

▲ Single-core PVC-insulated unsheathed cable

drawing into *trunking* and *conduit*; cable coloured brown or blue is used for single-phase systems and that with green and yellow stripes is used as a *circuit protective conductor* (*cpc*); also available in green, grey, yellow, white, black and red. Single-core PVC-insulated and sheathed cable (6181Y) is used for surface

▲ Single-core PVC-insulated and sheathed cable

wiring in situations with a low risk of mechanical damage, for example meter tails connecting the distribution board to the public electricity supply meter; also used for conduit and trunking runs in difficult environmental conditions. Single-core PVC-insulated and sheathed cable with a cpc (6241Y) is used for domestic and general wiring where a cpc is required for all circuits. PVC-insulated and sheathed flat-wiring cables (6242Y and 6243Y) are used for domestic and industrial wiring and for service wiring in situations with a low risk

▲ PVC-insulated and sheathed flat-wiring cables

of mechanical damage. Three-core cables include an uninsulated plain copper between the cores of twin cables and between the black and grey cores of three core cables. PVC-insulated and sheathed flexible cords (3092Y and 3093Y) are used in temperatures up to 85°C, but they are not suitable for use with heating appliances. PVC-insulated and sheathed flat twin flexible cord is used for table lamps, radios and TV sets where the cable may lie on the floor, but not to be used with heating appliances. PVC-insulated bell wire is used for wiring bells, alarms and other extra low voltage (*ELV*) indicators.

PVC conduit

A polyvinyl chloride (PVC) protective enclosure for cable runs in areas such as farm milking parlours. PVC conduit may be cut with a junior hacksaw and jointed with a PVC solvent adhesive. The joint is weatherproof and ideal for surface installations and variations of temperature. Provision for expansion should be made using expansion couplers.

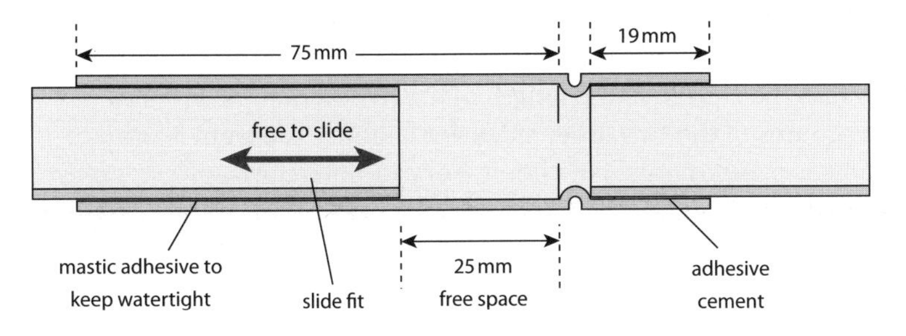

▲ PVC conduit with expansion provision in conduits

PVC-covered MICC

PVC-covered mineral-insulated copper cable (*MICC*).

PVC/GSWB/PVC cable

Polyvinyl chloride/galvanised steel wire braided/polyvinyl chloride cable has individual conductors inside an aluminium screen covered by an inner sheath, then a steel braid, and an outer sheath of PVC. The steel braid provides flexibility. This cable is very durable and is used in instrumentation applications or in signal applications where shielding is required.

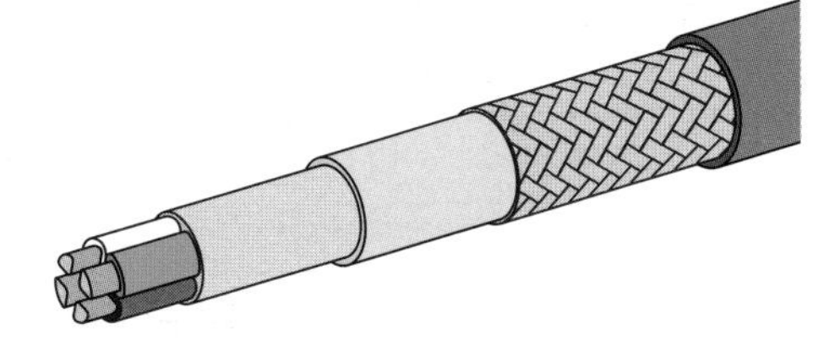

▲ PVC/GSWB/PVC cable

A B C D E F G H I J K L M N O P Q R S T U V W X Y Z

PVC trunking

Lighter and easier to handle than metal trunking, and used mainly for data cabling or computer supplies in locations such as shops and offices.

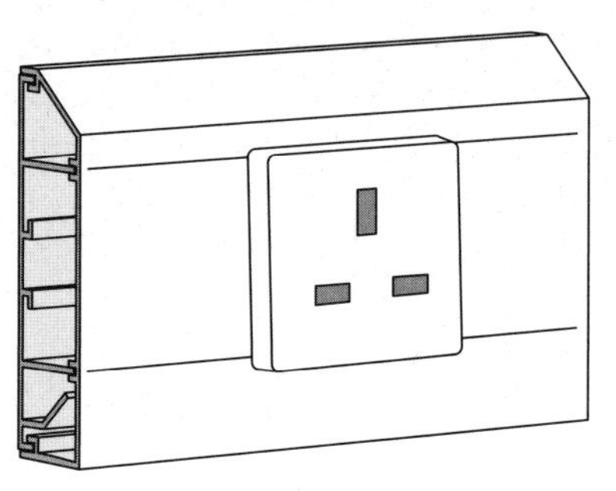

▲ PVC trunking

Pythagoras' theorem

In a right-angled triangle, the longest side is called the *hypotenuse*. Pythagoras' theorem states that the square of the length of the hypotenuse is equal to the sum of the squares of the two other sides. Pythagoras' theorem is used to calculate the power components in a circuit. For example, the *apparent power* would be given by:

$$(VA)^2 = (W)^2 + (VA_r)^2.$$

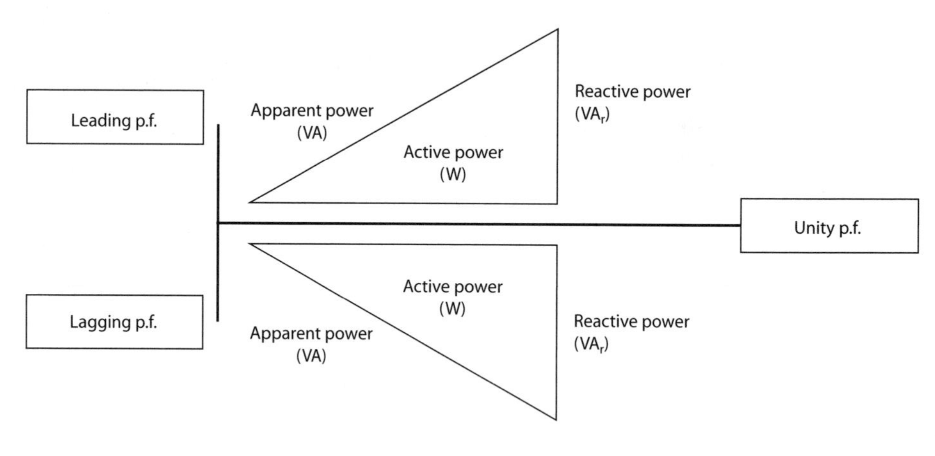

▲ The power triangle

quad processor

A device which allows four camera images to be viewed on one screen at the same time.

See *CCTV*

quick fix box (q.f.b.)

A plastic box used in dry lined walls to enable flush fitting of accessories. Tightening of the accessory fixing screws anchors the box into the wall.

quick start circuit

A circuit that is used to start a *fluorescent lamp* quickly. In this type of starter the electrodes are rapidly pre-heated by the end windings of an *autotransformer* so that a 'quick start' is possible.

radial circuit

A circuit in which the conductors finish at the last outlet without forming a loop. In an A2 radial circuit, the rating of the *overcurrent protection* device (30 A or 32 A *cartridge fuse* or *MCB*) determines the cable current rating. This circuit requires 4 mm^2 copper-conductor *PVC cables* or 2.5 mm^2 *MICC* cable. The floor area served must be less than 75 m^2. In an A3 radial circuit, used in domestic premises, 2.5 mm^2 copper cable must be used with a 20 A protective device and a floor area less than 50 m^2 in which any number of sockets may be installed.

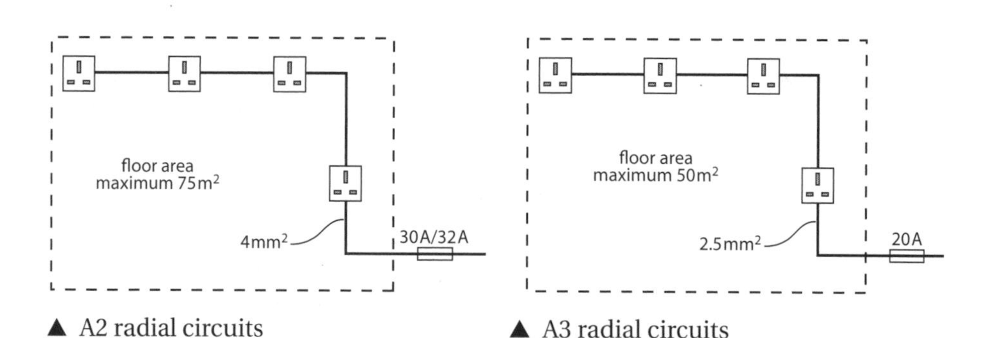

▲ A2 radial circuits ▲ A3 radial circuits

radiant heaters

Heaters which reflect heat, such as:

- a traditional electric fire, with a heating element on insulated blocks and a highly polished reflective surface
- an *infrared* heater, which has an iconel-sheathed element or a nickel-chrome spiral element in a glass silica tube mounted in front of a highly polished surface

- an oil-filled radiator, which has a pressed steel casing that houses the heating elements and the whole unit is filled with oil
- a tubular heater, which is a low-temperature unit which supplements the main heating and has a 50 mm mild steel or aluminium tube with a heating element mounted inside
- underfloor heating, where heating elements are installed under the floor and heat the tiles on the surface.

Radioactive Substances Act

The use of radioactive substances is covered by the Radioactive Substances Act 1993 (RSA 1993). This legislation is enforced by the Environment Agency. Very small amounts of radioactive substances can be found in fire alarms, smoke and heat detectors.

radio-frequency interference (RFI)

This is often caused by pulse-width modulation (PWM) circuits. The interference may be reduced by using short leads or additional filters on the power supply leads.

RCBO

See *Residual current circuit breaker with overload protection*

RCD

See *Residual current device*

reactive current

A current in either a *capacitive* or *inductive circuit*, which has no *resistance* or energy dissipation.

reactive power

Power used by reactive components, such as *capacitors* or *inductors*, and returned to source when the *current* is reversed. Reactive power is measured in volt-amperes-reactive (VAr).

See also *Active power*; *Apparent power*; *Power factor*; *True power*

record (as fitted) drawing

In some installations it is not possible to follow the original plans exactly. Issues may arise on site resulting in *conduit* being fixed in a different position or cables being routed a different way. The changes must be recorded on a drawing which shows how the installation was actually fitted. The 'as fitted' drawing is supplied by the consulting engineer at the end of the project with the actual conduit and *trunking* routes marked, and provides an essential reference for future maintenance or alterations, especially when the installation is hidden in the walls.

A B C D E F G H I J K L M N O P Q R S T U V W X Y Z

A B C D E F G H I J K L M N O P Q R S T U V W X Y Z

rectification

The conversion of an *a.c.* supply into a *d.c.* supply, as required for electronic circuits and equipment. Half-wave rectification is used mainly for battery charging. A *diode* only allows *current* to flow in one direction; in an a.c. circuit, only the positive half-cycles pass through the diode, resulting in a signal with a series of pulses. A *transformer* is installed at the supply side to ensure the required level of output *voltage*.

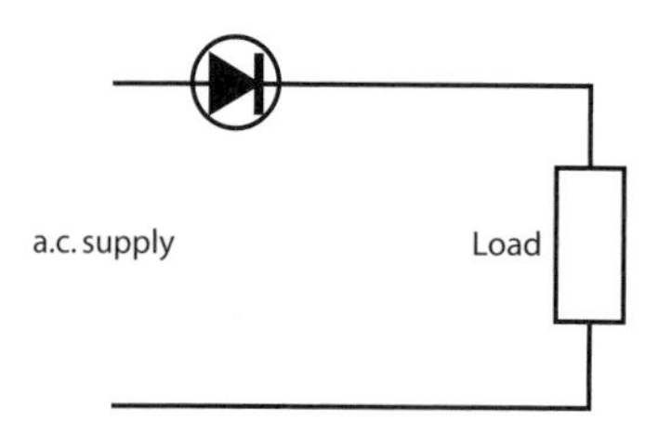

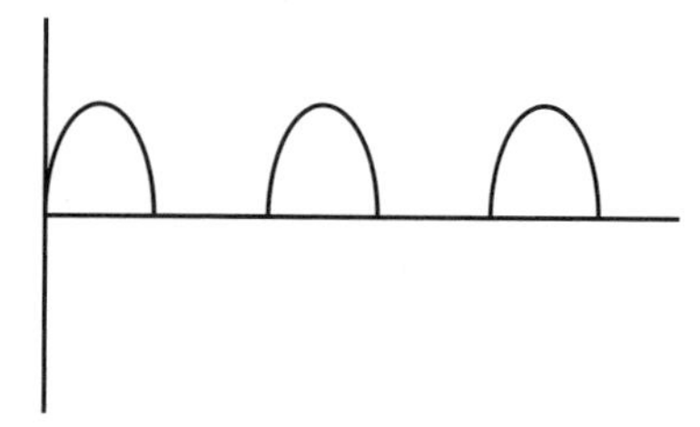

▲ Half-wave rectification

Full-wave rectification, in which two diodes are connected together to give a more even supply, is called a biphase circuit. The anodes of the diodes are connected to the opposite ends of the secondary winding of a centre-tapped transformer. The anode voltages are 180° *out of phase* with each other, so one diode rectifies the positive half-cycle and one rectifies the negative half-cycle. The output current is a series of pulses much closer together.

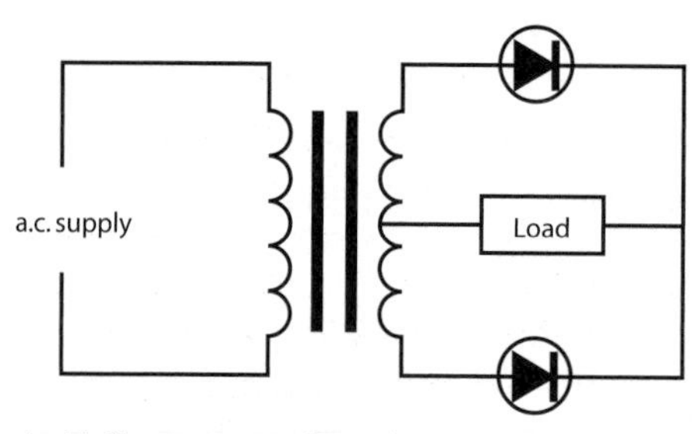

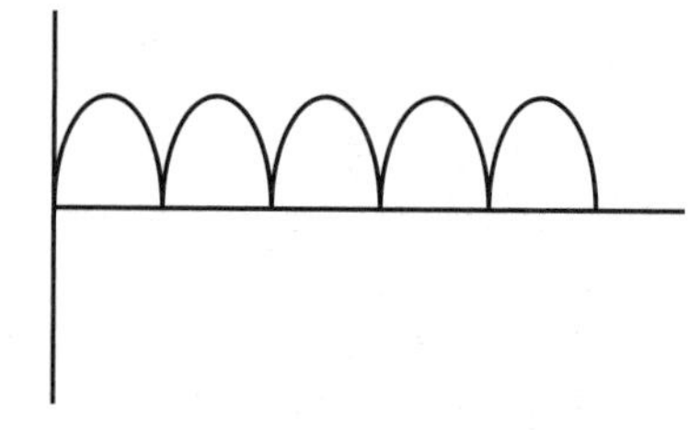

▲ Full-wave rectification

Regulations

General industry rules in place to ensure good practice. It is important to know which Regulations apply to your work, and to make regular checks for updates and new editions of relevant publications. Many were published by the IEE, which became the IET (Institution of Engineering and Technology) in 2006, so publications will be redesignated in due course. Regulations that every electrician should be aware of include:

- Electricity at Work Regulations 1989
- Health and Safety at Work Act 1974

- Electricity Safety, Quality and Continuity Regulations 2002
- Institution of Electrical Engineers (IEE) Wiring Regulations (BS 7671)
- IEE On-site Guide.

The IEE (now IET) publish a set of guidance notes, which are regularly updated and which simplify BS 7671 requirements:

- Guidance Note 1: Selection and Erection of Equipment
- Guidance Note 2: Isolation and Switching
- Guidance Note 3: Inspection and Testing
- Guidance Note 4: Protection against Fire
- Guidance Note 5: Protection against Electric Shock
- Guidance Note 6: Protection against Overcurrent
- Guidance Note 7: Special Locations.

relay

An electromechanical switch. A relay creates a *magnetic field* which opens or closes a contact or several sets of contacts. Relays can be used to control: a high-voltage circuit with a low-voltage signal; a high-current circuit with a low-current signal; a mains-powered device from a low-voltage switch.

remanence

The *flux density* remaining in magnetic material when the *magnetic field* has reduced to zero.

See *Coercivity*; *Hysteresis*

remote stop/start control

Remote stop/start controls are used, for example, in college workshops where emergency stop buttons are located throughout the workshop and can be activated to break the supply to a motor. They are also used when the environment around a motor is hazardous. The remote start/stop control usually has the start and stop buttons connected in series. As shown in the diagram, the remote start button is in parallel with the start button on the main enclosure. The supply to both buttons is routed through the stop button of the remote station.

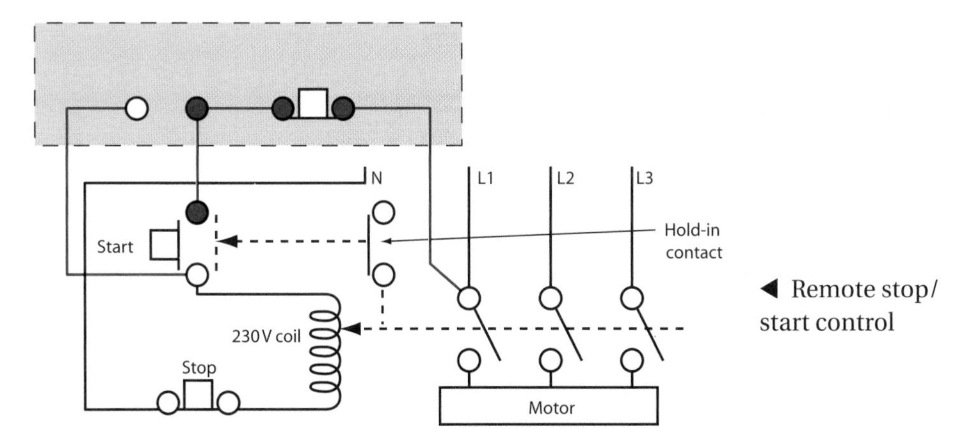

◀ Remote stop/start control

A B C D E F G H I J K L M N O P Q R S T U V W X Y Z

A B C D E F G H I J K L M N O P Q R S T U V W X Y Z

remote switching

The control of an electrical load using a control circuit, usually via a *contactor*. This remote switching capability allows heavy loads to be switched using devices that are only capable of switching much smaller currents – the contactor takes the heavy load current and the switching device, for instance a *photocell*, only needs to switch the current used by the contactor coil.

residual current circuit beaker with overload protection (RCBO)

A device which combines a *residual current device (RCD)* and a *miniature circuit breaker (MCB)*. The RCBO protects against the effects of *earth fault*, *overload* and *short circuit currents*, and reduces the number of outgoing ways required within a distribution board. Earth fault protection is restricted to a single circuit, so that supply is interrupted only in the circuit with the fault. A range of RCBOs are available: 10 A/30 mA, 16 A/30 mA, 20 A/30 mA, 32 A/30 mA and 40 A/30 mA.

residual current device (RCD)

A device which reduces the risk of *electric shock* by monitoring the *current* flowing in phase and neutral conductors. The device is set to trip if there is an *earth fault* which creates a difference above the set level. The RCD operates on low current, but the combination of this current and a high *earth-fault loop impedance* causes the potential in earthed metalwork to increase to dangerous levels. The *voltage* resulting from the operating current and earth-fault loop impedance must never exceed 50V. Most RCDs are built into the main switchboard or the socket outlet. A plug with a built-in RCD, or a plug-in RCD adaptor, will provide additional safety. The usual trip level set for an RCD is 30 milliamps (mA) and is shown as IΔn.

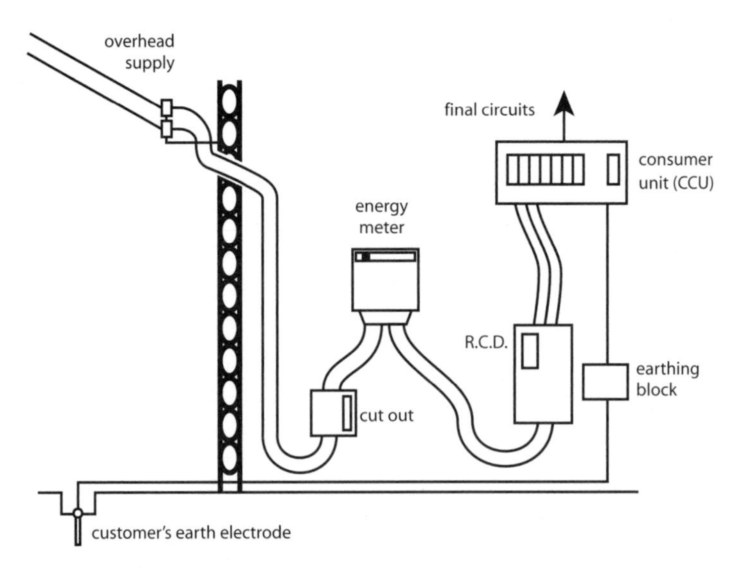

▲ Intake earthing arrangements on a TT system

resistance (R)

The level of opposition to the flow of *d.c.* current in a circuit measured in ohms. Resistance is measured using an *ohmmeter*. Resistance can be calculated using *Ohm's Law*.

$$R = \frac{V}{I}$$

In an *a.c.* circuit, *inductance* and *capacitance* will create further opposition, which, when combined with resistance (using *Pythagoras' theorem*) is termed *impendance*.

See *Capacitive circuit*; *Inductive circuit*

resistance/capacitance (RC) in series

In this type of circuit, a *resistor* is connected in series with a *capacitor* and fed from an *a.c.* supply. The flow of *current* (I) through the resistor and the capacitor is the same. This causes a *voltage drop* or *potential difference* across the resistor (V_R) and across the capacitor (V_C). The voltage lags behind the current by an amount determined by the values of the resistance and *capacitive reactance*.

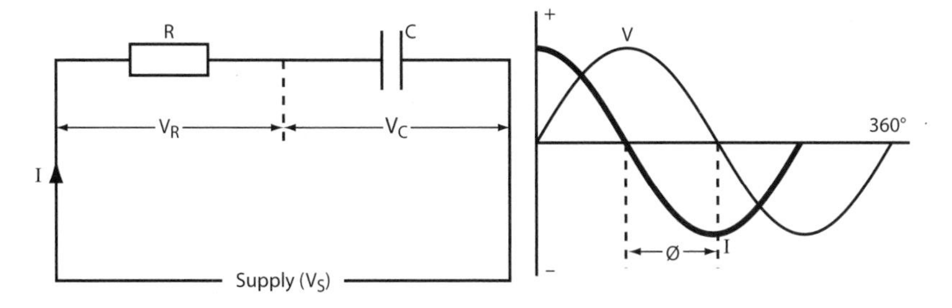

▲ A resistor connected in series with a capacitor, fed from an a.c. supply

resistance/inductance (RL) in series

In this type of circuit, a *resistor* is connected in series with an *inductor* and fed from an *a.c.* supply. The current (I) through the resistor and the inductor is the same. This causes a voltage drop across the resistor (V_R) and across the inductor (V_L). The current lags the voltage by an amount determined by the values of the resistance and *inductive reactance*.

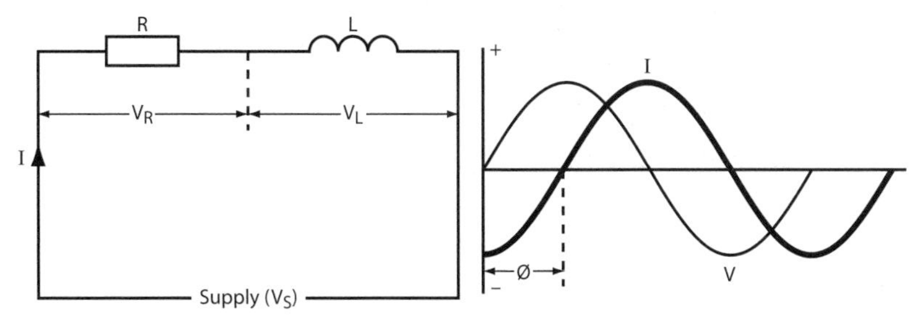

▲ Resistor and inductor in series

A B C D E F G H I J K L M N O P Q R S T U V W X Y Z

resistance, inductance and capacitance in parallel

In this circuit, the voltage (V_S) is the same to all branches of the circuit. The current through the *resistor* is in phase with the voltage, the current through the *inductor* lags the voltage by 90° and the current through the *capacitor* leads the voltage by 90°. Whether the total circuit current lags or leads the voltage depends on the relative values of *inductance* and *capacitance*.

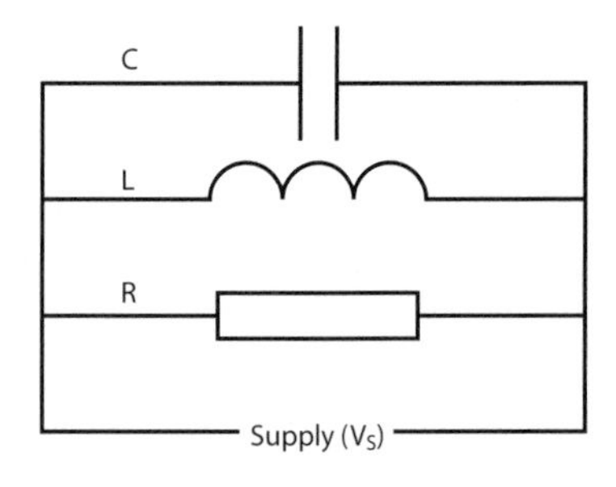

▲ Resistor, capacitor and inductor in parallel connected to an a.c. supply

resistance, inductance and capacitance in series (RLC)

In this circuit a *resistor* is connected in series with an *inductor* and a *capacitor*. This type of circuit may be referred to as an RLC, or a general series, circuit. The current (I) to all three components is the same, causing a voltage drop across the resistor (V_R), the inductor (V_L) and the capacitor (V_C). Whether the current lags or leads the supply voltage depends on the relative values of *inductance* and *capacitance*.

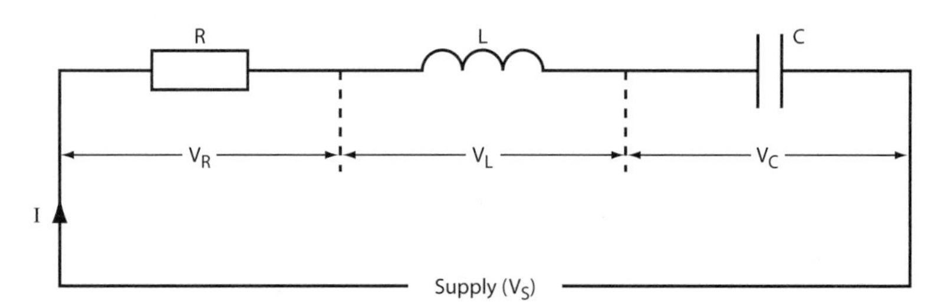

▲ Resistor connected in series with an inductor and capacitor, fed from an a.c. supply

resistive circuit

A circuit connected to an a.c. supply with no *capacitance* or *inductance*. The voltage and current have a *zero phase angle*. In practice, there will always be some capacitance and inductance.

resistivity

This is the general ability of an individual material to resist the flow of current. Resistivity is represented by the Greek symbol rho (ρ) and measured in micro-ohm millimetres (μΩmm). The resistivity of copper is 17.8 μΩmm, and for aluminium, rho (ρ) is 28.5 μΩmm. The resistance in a conductor length 'l' and cross-sectional area 'a' is given by the formula:

$$R = \frac{\rho l}{a}$$

resistor

A component in a circuit which provides non-reactive opposition to the flow of current. Resistors may be fixed, where the resistance value cannot be changed mechanically (but may be affected by temperature), or variable, where a spindle or slider is included for adjusting the resistance value. A fixed resistor may be produced by winding brass wire on to a rod of insulating material, then covering the wire with a coating for protection from damage. The *resistance* value depends on the length and cross-sectional area of the wire and its *resistivity*. Wire-wound variable resistors use a flat strip of insulating material, rather than a rod. This is wrapped to form almost a complete circle and a sliding contact arm is attached which contacts the turns of wire.

Resistors are often marked with coloured bands to indicate the value of the resistance.

See *potentionmeter*

Resistor colour code

Band colour	Value
Black	0
Brown	1
Red	2
Orange	3
Yellow	4
Green	5
Blue	6
Violet	7
Grey	8
White	9
Gold	0.1
Silver	0.01

▲ Resistor colour code

rewirable fuse

A fuse made up of a piece of wire held between two screw terminals within a porcelain or bakelite holder and carrier. The fuse holder is marked with a colour code to show which circuits the fuse is designed for: 5 A is white; 15 A is blue; 20 A is yellow; 30 A is red; 45 A is green. Rewirable fuses must conform to standard *BS 3036*.

ring circuit

A circuit in which the phase, neutral and *circuit protective conductors* are connected at the consumer unit, looped into each socket outlet in turn and returned to the consumer unit, forming a ring. This means that each socket outlet has two connections to the mains supply. Any number of socket outlets could be installed, as long as:

- each outlet of twin or multiple sockets is regarded as one socket outlet
- the floor area served by a single 30 A or 32 A ring final circuit must not exceed 100 m^2

- kitchens and utility rooms may require separate circuits
- when more than one ring circuit is installed, the socket outlets should be shared so that the load is balanced
- diversity should comply with Table 8A of the IEE *Guidance Notes*
- immersion heaters, large storage vessels and permanently connected heating appliances must have a separate circuit.

ring circuit continuity test

This test establishes that the ring does exist and is connected correctly. The IEE Wiring *Regulations* require that a section of the ring is tested. To ensure that this is done, each conductor should be marked at the distribution board as either an incoming section from the last socket, or an outgoing section to the first. The reading at each socket should be about the same. If one socket has a higher reading, then there is a *spur* connected to that socket using additional cable outside the ring.

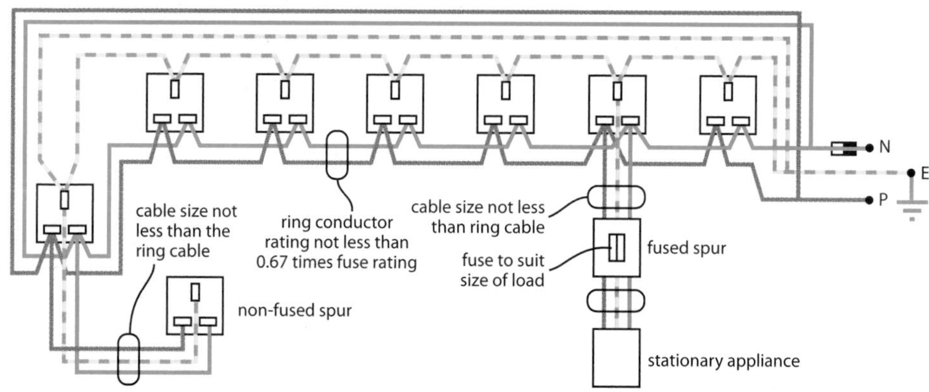

▲ Domestic ring circuit with spurs

ring final circuit conductors continuity testing

This is a circuit wiring test conducted using a low-resistance *ohmmeter*, which shows up open circuits and interconnections within the wiring. Readings should be between 0.01 and 0.1 ohms. A correctly wired circuit will produce the same reading at each point. A different reading at one or several points indicates a probable open circuit or interconnections; these faults may cause an overload on part of the circuit wiring.

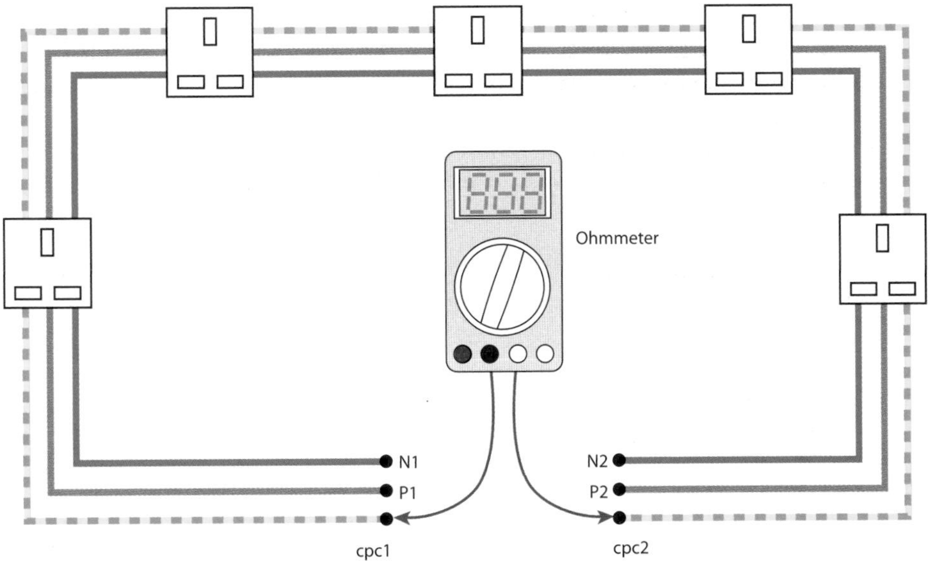

Ohmmeter
N1
P1
cpc1
N2
P2
cpc2

▲ Measurement of phase, neutral and protective conductors

RLC circuit

See *Resistance inductance capacitance in series (RLC)*

rms (root mean square)

This value is the effective voltage or current – the *a.c.* equivalent of a *d.c.* quantity which would deliver the same average power to the same *resistor*. The formula for working out rms:

$$\text{rms} = 0.707 \times \text{peak current or voltage}$$

See *Average value*; *Peak value*

rotor

An *a.c. generator* has a stationary armature known as the stator and a rotating element called the rotor, which carries a rotating *magnetic field*. There are two main types of rotor, the *squirrel-cage rotor* and the *wound rotor*.

rotor-resistance starter

A starter used with a *slip-ring motor* when the motor starts against full load. An external *resistance* is connected to the rotor windings to increase the starting *torque*. When the motor is switched on, the initial external rotor resistance is at the maximum level, but as the motor speeds up the resistance reduces. At full speed the external resistance is nil and the machine runs as an induction motor with a *squirrel-cage rotor*.

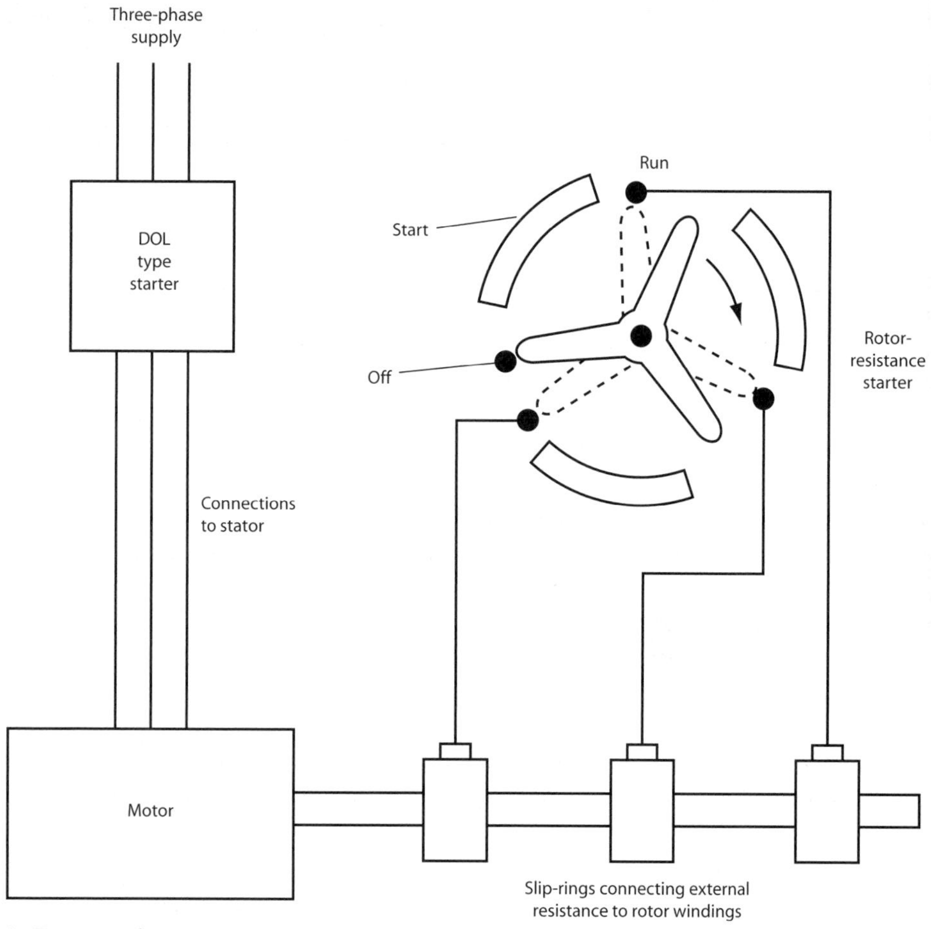

▲ Rotor-resistance starter

safety, electrical

The safety of electrical installations is vital, that is, it is essential for life. One of the standards for the installation of new electrical systems is BS 7671 Requirements for Electrical Installations. The system must also be maintained in a safe condition. Safe electrical equipment should be used and it must also be properly maintained. Some electrical safety tips include:

- provide sufficient socket outlets
- use equipment suitable for the working environment
- use air-, hydraulic-, hand- or battery-powered tools when appropriate
- ensure that equipment is safe and maintained in a safe condition
- inspect and test portable equipment (*PAT*)
- provide accessible and labelled off switches for fixed machines
- use the nearest suitable socket outlet for portable equipment
- replace damaged sections of cable completely
- reduce the voltage to the lowest needed to get the job done
- research all the relevant safety *Regulations* and guidelines before starting a new task.

scaled drawing

Layout and assembly drawing where all measurements are based on a fixed ratio to the actual size of the object. A 1:100 scale means that every measurement on the drawing is 100 times smaller than the actual measurements. The actual measurement on the object will be equal to distance on the drawing multiplied by the scale.

schematic diagram

A simplified working diagram used for large, complex electrical installations, giving an overview of the components and connections of a system and using industry symbols. Schematic diagrams are not drawn to scale, for example railway or underground maps.

A B C D E F G H I J K L M N O P Q R S T U V W X Y Z

scissor lift

A mobile elevating platform with compact dimensions and a tight turning circle, used to gain access for a range of installation and maintenance tasks. A safety harness, attached to the lift, must be worn at all times.

▲ Scissor lift

screw rule

A method used to determine the direction of a *magnetic field*. Using the example of a right-hand threaded screw, the direction of movement of the tip represents the direction of the *current* and the direction of rotation of the screw represents the rotation of the magnetic field.

screwit

Old porcelain connector with internal threads which was used to joint cables with different types of insulator. Screwits may be found on old installations.

Seebeck effect

A thermal effect which causes an *electromotive force*, discovered by Thomas Johann Seebeck in 1821. A closed circuit with two junctions made between two metals at different temperatures produces a *potential difference*. If a *voltmeter* is connected to the cooler end and heat is applied to the other, the reading will depend upon the difference in temperature. Metals arranged in this pattern produce a *thermocouple* and may be used to measure temperatures. The hot end is placed inside an oven or hot-water system and the cold end is connected to a remote meter.

self-inductance

When a *conductor* is formed into a coil and carries an alternating *current*, the *magnetic field* created around the coil will increase and decrease in relation to the changing current. This induces an *e.m.f.* into the coils which is in opposition to the voltage that created it.

See *Inductance*

SELV (separate extra low voltage)

See *ELV (extra low voltage)*

semiconductor

A semiconductor is a material which is neither a good electrical *conductor* nor a good electrical *insulator*. Semiconductor materials such as silicon or germanium have atoms arranged in a lattice structure, with the atoms equidistant and bonded to adjacent atoms. Each atom has four *valence electrons* but no free electrons. An impurity must be added to allow conduction to take place. Adding a pentavalent material such as arsenic introduces an extra electron to the semiconductor, creating a surplus negative charge; the material is called n-type. Adding a trivalent material such as aluminium to the semiconductor removes an electron, producing a surplus positive charge; the material is called p-type.

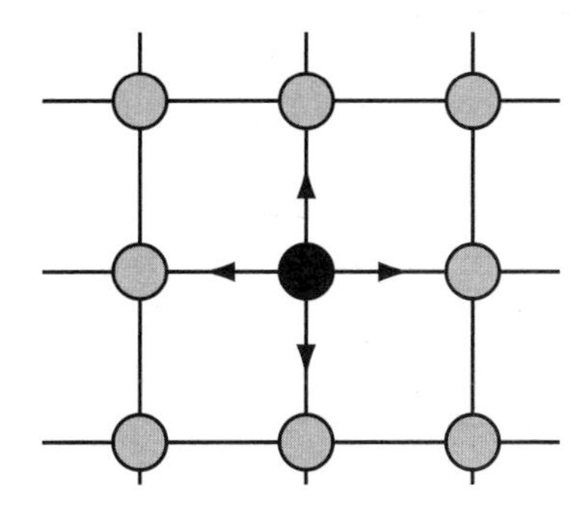

▲ Lattice structure of a semi-conducting material

semi-resonant starter

In the circuit for a semi-resonant starter for a *fluorescent lamp* (discharge lighting), the *choke* is replaced by a *transformer* with the secondary coil wound in opposition to the primary coil. The current flows through the primary coils to one cathode of the lamp, then through the secondary coil and a large *capacitor* to the second cathode of the lamp, which is connected to neutral. The current heats the cathodes and the pre-start current leads the voltage owing to the circuit being predominantly *capacitive*. The voltages across the coil windings are 180° *out of phase*, so the voltage across the tube is increased, causing the arc to strike. The primary windings behave as a choke, stabilising the current in the arc. The circuit has the advantage of high *power factor* and easy starting at low temperatures.

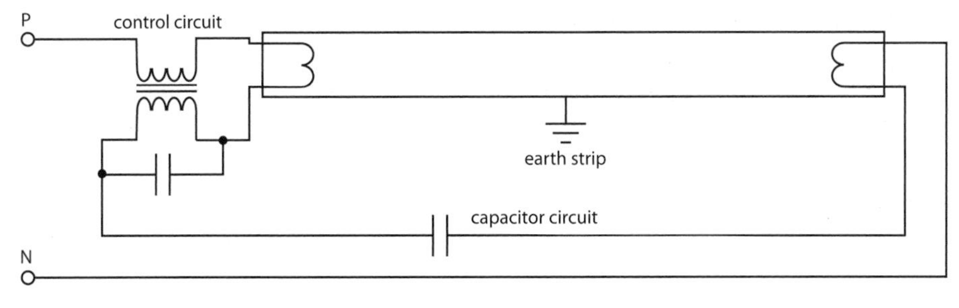

▲ Semi-resonant circuit

separate extra low voltage (SELV)

See *ELV (extra low voltage)*

A
B
C
D
E
F
G
H
I
J
K
L
M
N
O
P
Q
R
S
T
U
V
W
X
Y
Z

series circuit

A circuit where the current can only take one route through the circuit, for example where a number of *resistors* are connected together end to end and then connected to a *battery*. The total *power* in a series circuit equals the sum of the individual powers used by each resistor. The *current* has the same value at every point in the circuit. The circuit resistance (R_T) is the sum of the individual resistors $R_1 + R_2 + R_3$. The total circuit current (I) is the supply voltage divided by the total resistance. The *potential difference* across each resistor is proportional to its resistance (*Ohm's law*):

$V_1 = \text{Current (I)} \times R_1$

$V_2 = \text{Current (I)} \times R_2$

$V_3 = \text{Current (I)} \times R_3$.

The supply voltage (V) is the sum of the potential differences across each resistor:

$V = V_1 + V_2 + V_3$

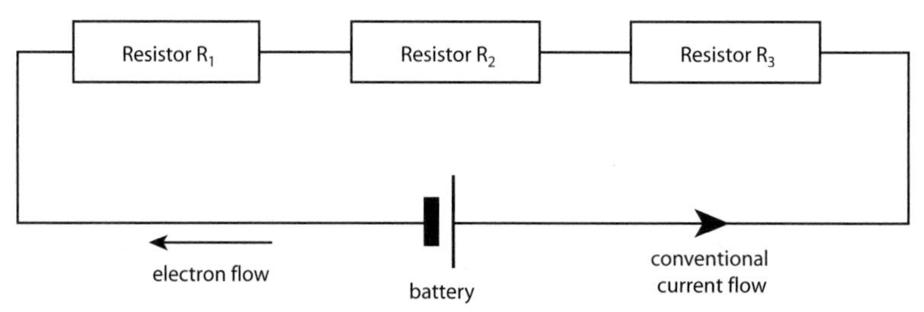

▲ Series circuit

series motor

A motor with the field coil wired in series with the *armature*. This type of motor may be used in both *d.c.* and *a.c.* situations. It has a high starting *torque* and a variable speed characteristic which means that the motor is useful for starting heavy loads. It is also called a series universal motor, series wound motor, or just a universal motor.

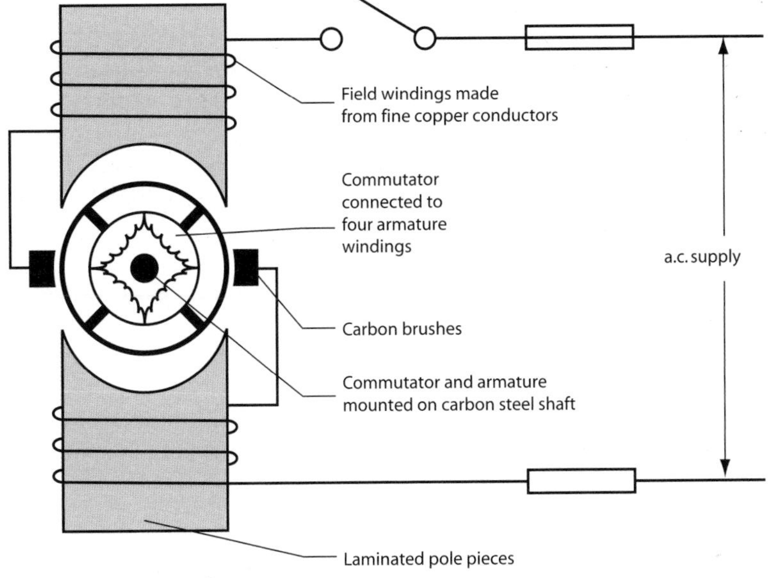

▲ Series universal motor

series/parallel circuit

A circuit which combines *series* and *parallel circuits*. The *resistance* is found by calculating the resistance of the parallel group and adding this value to the sum of series resistors in the circuit.

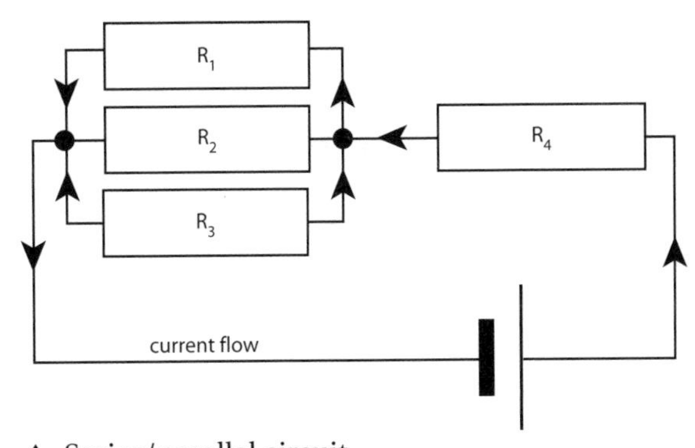

▲ Series/parallel circuit

A B C D E F G H I J K L M N O P Q R S T U V W X Y Z

shaded pole motor

A *single-phase induction motor* with one main winding and no start winding. The motor is started by a continuous copper loop wound around a small section of each motor pole, shading that portion of the pole. This causes the *magnetic field* in the wound section to lag the field in the unwound section. The two fields react and start the shaft rotating. This motor is simple and inexpensive and used for light-duty applications such as household fans.

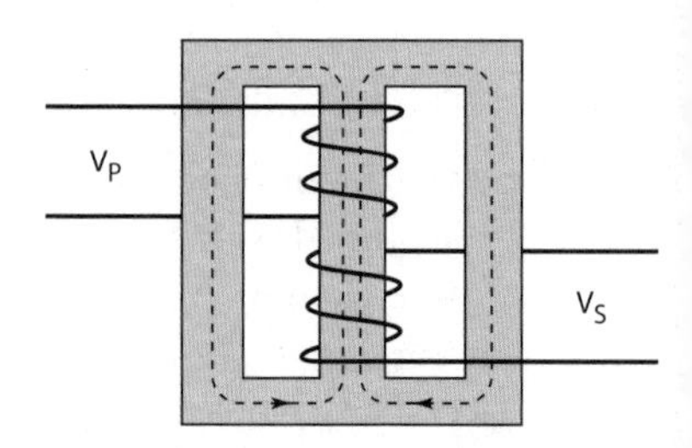

▲ Shell-type transformer

shell-type transformer

A *transformer* used to reduce magnetic flux leakage. Both windings are on the central leg of the transformer and the two outer legs provide parallel paths for the magnetic flux.

short circuit

A short circuit fault occurs when two live conductors come into contact. This may be caused by connection errors, equipment failure, moisture or accidents.

See *Prospective short circuit current (PSCC)*

shower, electric

The water for an electric shower is heated by an *instantaneous water heater*, which heats water only as required. The water flows through a small internal tank containing heating elements, and the water is heated to a higher temperature depending on the degree of water flow restriction. The electric shower water heater must be supplied through a dedicated *fuse* or *MCB* in the consumer unit and must have a double-pole *isolator* near the shower.

shunt motor

A type of *d.c. motor* which has the *armature* and field circuits wired in parallel providing constant field strength and motor speed.

silicon controlled rectifier (SCR)

See *Thyristor*

silicone rubber insulation

An inexpensive material which maintains the same level of *insulation* ability after being heated or burned. Silicone rubber FP 200 cable has an extruded aluminium over-sheath foil and is recommended for use on *fire alarm systems*.

simmerstat

An energy regulator which uses a bi metallic strip to control the temperature of electric cooking plates. An internal coil heats the bi metallic strip and opens and closes a switch. The time interval of the opening and closing of the switch is controlled through a knob on the front of the simmerstat, varying the length of time that power is supplied to the hotplate. The heater coil responds to the flow of current and controls the bi metallic strip. The two types of simmerstat are shunt connected and series connected.

The shunt-connected type has a two-part bi metallic strip block, where strip 'A' is wrapped with small-gauge heater wire-connected in parallel with the hotplate element and strip 'B' is touching the cam of the control knob. The strips are connected at one end and pivoted on point 'C'. In the off position, the cam pushes the bi metallic strip, keeping the contacts at 'F' open, and no current can flow. When turned on, the cam moves, reducing pressure on the bi metallic strip, causing the contacts at 'F' to close, current then flows and the hotplate starts to heat up. Current will also flow through the heater coil, bending the bi metallic stripand opening the contacts at 'F', and this stops the current. The cooling of the heater coil and bi metallic strip, bends the bi metallic strip back, closing the contacts at 'F' again. The cycle continues, repeatedly, switching power to the hotplate on and off and keeping the plate at constant temperature.

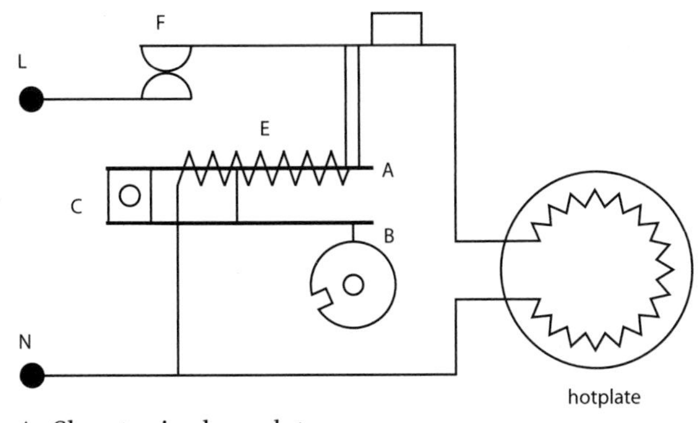

▲ Shunt-wired regulator

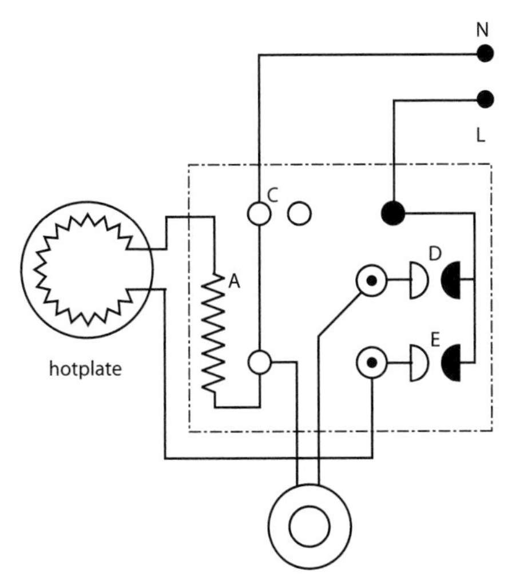

▲ Series-wired regulator

The series type of simmerstat has a bi metallic heater coil 'A' connected in series with the hotplate. The contacts at 'D' and 'E' close when the control knob is turned on. Contact 'D' joins a pilot lamp into the circuit to show that the hotplate is being heated. Contact 'E' energises the hotplate. When the heater coil 'A' transmits heat, the bi metallic strip bends, opening the contacts at 'C', so that the pilot lamp goes out and the hotplate is switched off. The heater coil then cools, bending the bi metallic strip back and closing the contacts at 'C'.

sine

A function of an angle in a right-angled triangle, the sine of an angle is equal to the ratio of the length of the side opposite the angle to the length of the *hypotenuse*.

sine wave

A waveform representation showing how a *current* or *voltage* varies with the *sine* of the elapsed time.

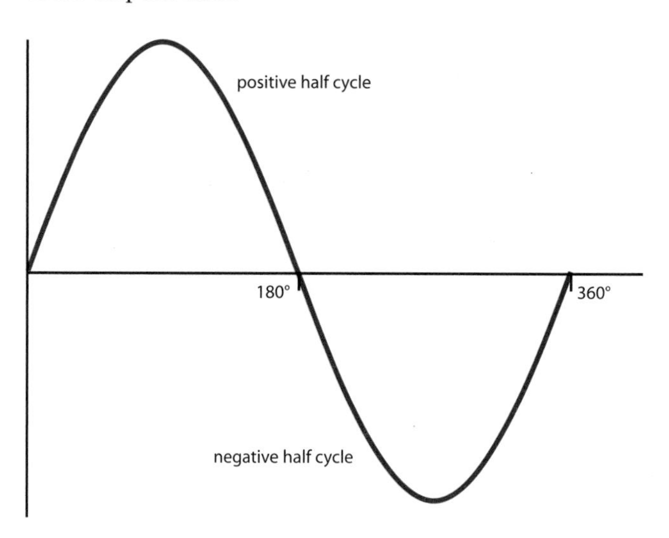

▲ Sine wave

single core PVC insulated sheathed cable

A cable type suitable for surface wiring where there is little risk of mechanical damage. The cable is normally used as meter tails for connecting the consumer unit to the supply meter. The *PVC cable* reference number is 6181Y.

single core PVC insulated unsheathed cable

A cable type designed for drawing into *trunking* and *conduits*. Its construction is that of a PVC insulated solid or stranded copper conductor, coloured brown or blue for single phase systems. The reference *PVC cable* number is 6491X.

single-phase a.c. synchronous motor

A small single-phase *a.c. motor* with magnetised rotor which does not need any induced current. The rotor rotates synchronously with the mains *frequency*. The speed of these motors is very accurate and they are used to power mechanical clocks, audio turntables and tape drives.

single-phase induction motor

A motor consisting of a laminated *stator* with single-phase windings arranged for split-phase starting, and a *squirrel cage rotor*, which is a laminated framework with copper or aluminium bars fitted into insulated longitudinal slots with the bars connected with metal end-rings.

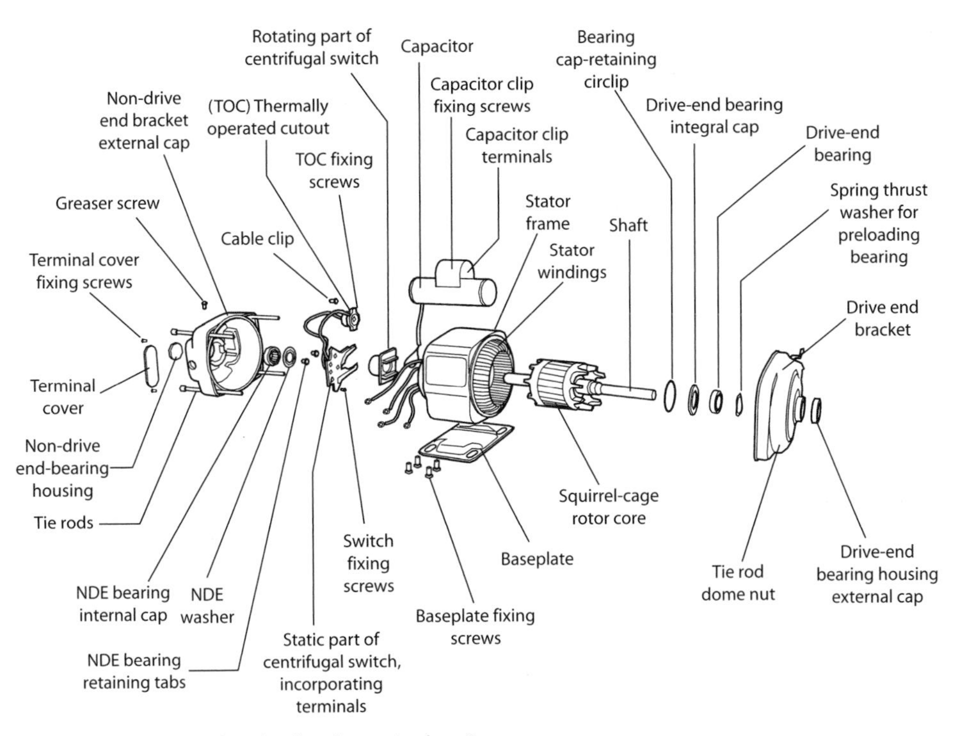

▲ Construction of a single-phase induction motor

slip-ring motor

See *Wound rotor*

smoke detector

A smoke detector should be fitted according to current Health and Safety guidelines. There are two types of smoke detector: an ionisation detector, which is very sensitive to smoke from burning paper or spirits as this usually contains fine particles, and an optical or photoelectric detector, which is sensitive to thick smoke with large particles, for example from burning plastic.

▲ Smoke detector

socket outlets inspection

See *Inspection checklists*

A
B
C
D
E
F
G
H
I
J
K
L
M
N
O
P
Q
R
S
T
U
V
W
X
Y
Z

soft starter

A reduced-voltage starter which lessens the starting *torque* for *a.c. induction motors*. The soft starter is connected in series with the supply to the motor, and uses solid state devices to control the current flow and voltage to the motor.

solar cell

See *Photodiode*

solenoid

A hollow cylinder, several times longer than its diameter, and closely wound around the outside with a uniform coil of wire. A *magnetic field* is created inside the cylinder when a *current* is sent through the wire. The magnetic field is similar to that of a bar magnet, and an iron rod placed partly inside the solenoid will be drawn further in when the current is turned on. The motion is used to move a lever or operate a latch. An electric switch can be used to energise a solenoid and produce a mechanical action at a remote location.

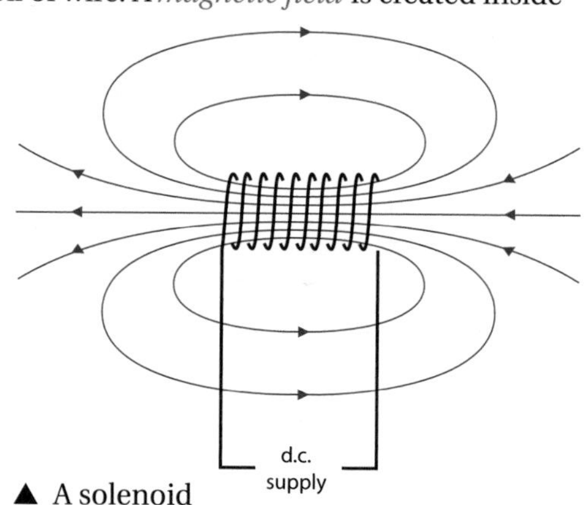

▲ A solenoid

solid state equipment

Solid state equipment includes *diodes*, *transistors*, *light emitting diodes (LEDs)*, *integrated circuits (IC)*, and *liquid crystal displays (LCD)*. This equipment operates within sensitive voltage and current ranges in millivolts and milliamperes. Most of the work required in this field is done by specialists. Electricians may come into contact with solid state equipment when testing installations and should ensure that the equipment is disconnected, as test voltages can damage the sensitive components.

space detection

Devices used to detect an intruder once they are past the perimeter protection and have gained entry to the premises.

See *Intruder alarm system*; *Passive infrared sensor*

space heating

Electric heating which is available as direct acting heaters or thermal storage devices. Direct acting heaters include *radiant* and *convection heaters* which are switched on and off as required or operated by a *thermostat*. Thermal storage devices heat up special blocks during off-peak times when electricity is less expensive. The stored heat is released as required.

special locations

Some locations are considered to present more than the average level of hazard and additional *Regulations*, BS 7671 Part 6, apply to these locations to ensure safety. The special locations include:

- areas with a bath or shower
- swimming pools and hot air saunas
- construction site installations
- restrictive conductive locations
- areas with high protective currents
- agricultural and horticultural locations
- caravans, motor homes and caravan parks
- highway power supplies, street furniture and street located equipment.

More information is given in IEE *Guidance Note* 7.

specialist installations

This is work that requires extra training or experience to carry out, such as: cable jointing, highway electrical systems, electrical machine drive installations, panel building, instrumentation, electrical maintenance.

split-phase motor

The split-phase motor has a second set of poles added to a *single-phase induction motor*, positioned 90° from the existing wiring around the stator. When the supply is connected, the two sets of windings, the start set and the run set, are both energised. The start winding has fewer turns of smaller wire and higher *resistance* which creates a small phase shift. The start winding current lags the run winding current by about 30°. The flux in the two windings grows and collapses at different times creating an apparent rotating *magnetic field* round the *rotor* and the motor begins to turn. When the motor reaches 75 per cent full load speed, the start winding is disconnected by a centrifugal switch attached to the shaft, and the motor operates from the run winding. The split-phase motor is mainly used on hand tools, grinders and fans.

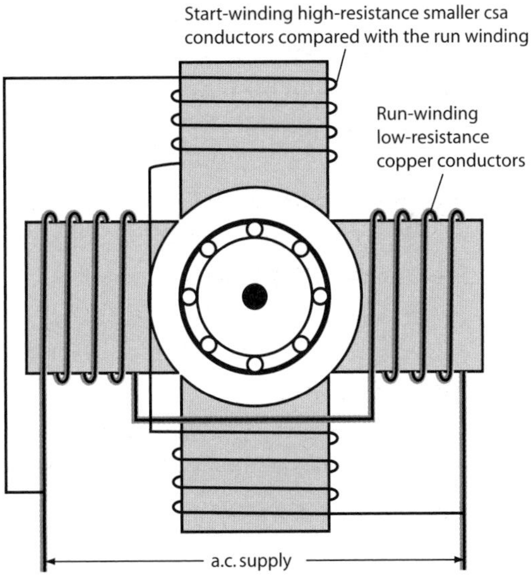

▲ Split-phase induction motor

A B C D E F G H I J K L M N O P Q R S T U V W X Y Z

sprinkler system

An integrated system of piping and sprinklers installed in an area or building to control or suppress a fire when activated. Water is released from the pipes or sprinklers through nozzles that open automatically with a rise in temperature. An alarm may also be triggered when the sprinklers are activated.

▲ Sprinkler

spur

A radial branch taken from a *ring circuit*.

squirrel cage motor

This is an *a.c. induction motor* which consists of two basic electrical assemblies: the wound *stator* and the *rotor* assembly (strictly, 'squirrel cage' only refers to the rotor). The bars of the rotor are shorted out with end rings at each end. This creates numerous circuits for the induced *e.m.f.* and resultant *current* to flow and produce the *magnetic field*. The rotor bars are encased in hundreds of thin insulated segments of silicon steel and skewed to increase resistance. The shaft has two low-friction bearings which allow the rotor to spin freely. The bearings and rotor are held within the yoke of the stator by two end caps secured by a nut and long bolt through the stator. The stator contains the field windings which produce the magnetic field in which the rotor operates.

See *Hand-operated star-delta starter*

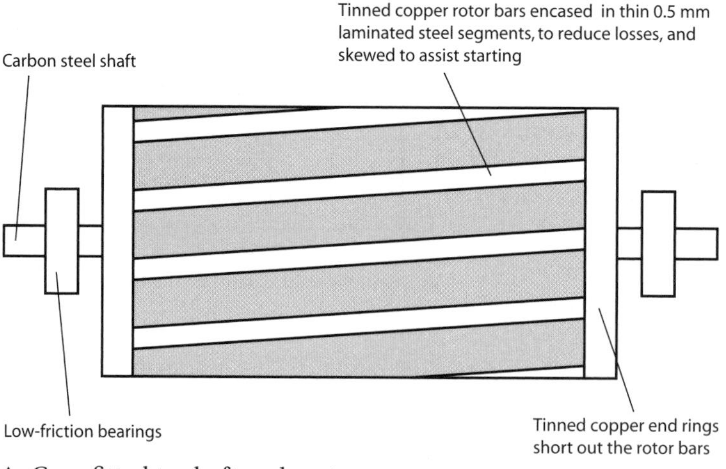

▲ Cage fitted to shaft and motor

standby lighting

A form of *emergency lighting* that is installed in public buildings to enable activities to continue if there is a power interruption. Emergency lighting must be installed in accordance with the BS 5266 Part 1: 1999 – Code of Practice for Emergency Lighting.

standby power supply

An independent generating system that some buildings have which is activated in the case of a complete power blackout. These systems are essential in locations such as hospitals. Smaller battery systems called *uninterruptible power supplies (UPS)* are used in offices to prevent loss of data in computer systems when the power supply is interrupted.

star connection

A three-phase system uses either three conductors (*delta connection*) or four (star connection). Star connection is used for an unbalanced load, where the *current* in each of the phases is different. One end of each of the three loops is connected to a central point also known as the star point. The neutral connection is taken from this point and connected to earth; this is the three-phase four-wire system. The star-connected system allows two voltages: one for connection between any two phases (400 V) and another for a connection between any phase and neutral (230 V). There is also 230 V between any phase and earth.

The diagram shows a star-connected three-phase load. The connection between phases is referred to as the line voltage and is shown as V_L. The phase voltage exists between any phase conductor and the neutral conductor and is shown as V_P. The line currents are represented by I_{BR}, I_{Gy} and I_{Bl}, and the phase currents are represented by I_P. The line and phase currents are the same, but the line voltage (400V) is greater than the phase voltage (230 V).

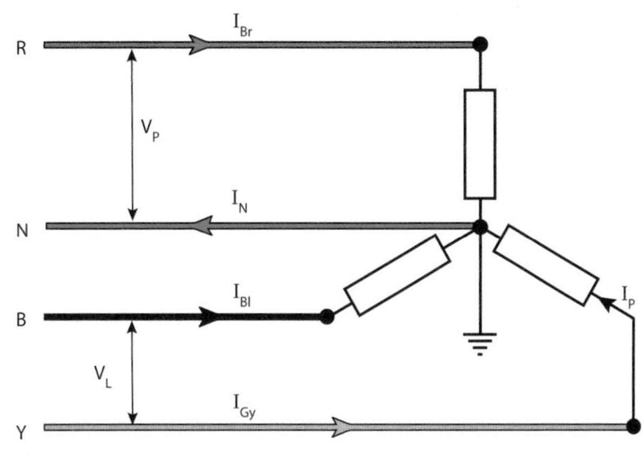

▲ Star connection

A B C D E F G H I J K L M N O P Q R S T U V W X Y Z

star delta

A system of connection in which a *star connection* switches to a *delta connection*. This type of connection may be used for *induction motors*.

starters – fluorescent lamps

The two main starters used in *fluorescent lamps* (discharge lighting) are *glow-type starters* and *semi-resonant starters*. In the glow-type starter a set of open contacts mounted on *bi metallic strips* are contained in helium gas. When power is applied, a glow discharge around the open contacts heats up the bi metallic strips which bend and connect. The electrodes at either end of the fluorescent tube are then in circuit and heat up giving off a cloud of electrons. The *choke* in the circuit builds up an intense *magnetic field*. When the contacts touch, the glow in the starter stops and the bi metallic strips cool and move apart, which momentarily breaks the circuit. The magnetic field in the choke collapses rapidly, this produces a high back *e.m.f.* which provides the high voltage required for *ionisation* of the gas. The main discharge across the lamp then takes place. The glow-type starter does not always work first time and often makes the light flash on and off before starting.

See *Semi-resonant starter*

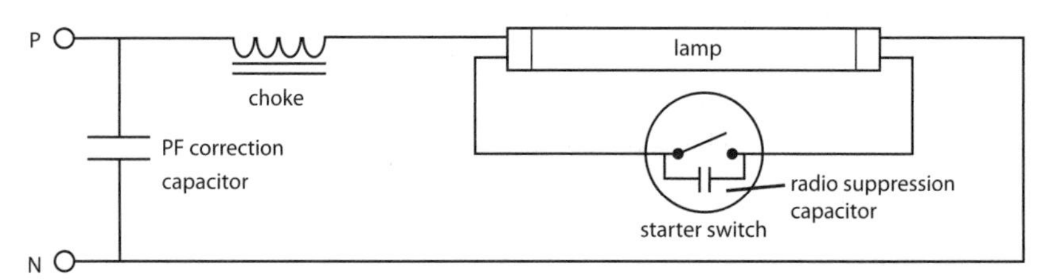

▲ Glow-type starter circuit

stator

The stationary part of a rotating machine (motor or generator). The stator usually contains the field winding which produces the *magnetic field* in which the *rotor* (rotating component) revolves.

statutory

Relating to the legal requirements for work practices and standards. A statutory authority is a body set up and empowered by legislation.

storage battery

An emergency energy source in the event of power failure, for example batteries to power *emergency lighting* and alarm panels, IT *uninterruptible power supply* (*UPS*) systems and starting for standby generators. The hazards involved with storage batteries include:

- corrosive acid in lead-acid cell batteries which is harmful to the skin and eyes and should be immediately diluted and cleansed by frequent bathing with fresh water

- hydrogen emitted when lead acid cells are charged, explosive when mixed with air
- applying high voltages to cell terminals will damage the battery
- shorts across terminals when connecting cells produce arcing, which can cause an explosion
- disconnection of cells may also produce arcing, which could cause an explosion.

strap saddle (half saddle)

A support used for fixing *conduit* to a cable tray or steel framework.

street lighting

The use of electricity to illuminate the public highways to a set level, also known as *highway power supplies*. It typically uses discharge lighting set high on lamp standards and is switched via a *photocell*.

The IEE wiring *regulations* include special requirements for highway power supplies.

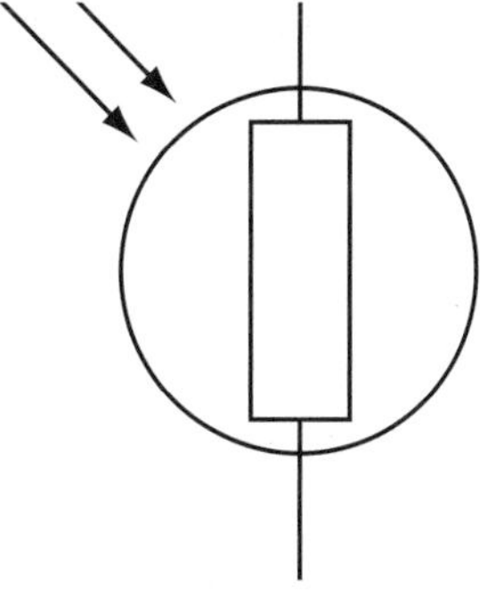

▲ Photocell circuit symbol

strip connector

A conductor terminal where the conductors are fixed by brass grub screws in the connectors which are mounted in an insulated block. A tight termination avoids high-resistance contacts which would result in the joint overheating.

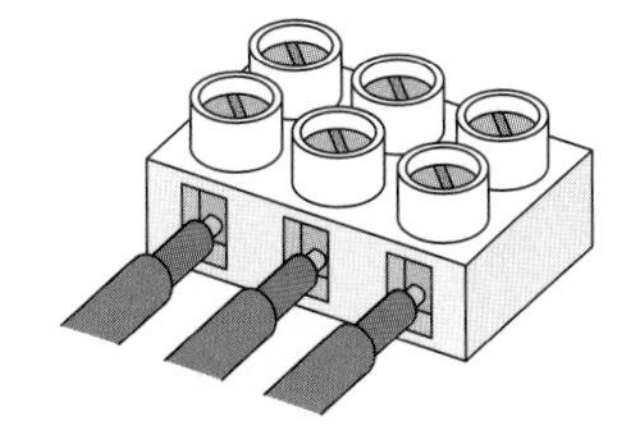

▲ Strip connector

strobe light

See *Xenon lamp*

stroboscopic effect

A flickering effect produced in *fluorescent lamps* by the discharge across the electrodes being extinguished at a rate of 100 times per second. This stroboscopic effect can be hazardous, for example it distorts the actual appearance of rotating machinery so that it seems to have slowed down, changed direction or stopped. There are also effective uses of the effect, for example calibrating speed measurement devices. The stroboscopic effect can be reduced or eradicated using locally fitted tungsten filament lamps or by having adjacent fluorescent fittings connected to different phases of the supply.

A B C D E F G H I J K L M N O P Q R S T U V W X Y Z

switches, testing

It is recommended that a thorough internal visual inspection of a random sample of 10 per cent or more of all switching devices is conducted to ensure good electrical and mechanical condition. In the event of there being any signs of damage due to arcing or overheating then all the switches associated with the installation should be inspected.

switchgear

This equipment is also known as control equipment and includes switchgear installed just after the metering equipment, for example:

- double-pole switch in consumer unit (domestic)
- single-phase double-pole switch fuse (industrial)
- three-phase triple-pole and neutral switch fuse (industrial)
- moulded case circuit breakers – polyphase switch rooms (large industrial).

symbols

See *Layout diagram symbols*

synchronous a.c. induction motor

See *Single-phase a.c. synchronous motor*; *Three-phase a.c. synchronous motor*

synchronous speed

The synchronous (n_s) refers to the speed of the rotating *magnetic field* in an *a.c. motor*. The difference between this and speed of the rotor is called slip. n_s depends on the number of *pole pairs* and the *frequency* of the supply. The synchronous speed is calculated by:

$$n_s \text{ (revolutions per second)} = \frac{\text{Frequency (f) in Hz}}{\text{Number of pole pairs (p)}}$$

synthetic rubber insulation

Synthetic rubber, such as *vulcanised butyl rubber*, can withstand very high temperatures and is recommended for connecting immersion heaters, storage heaters and boiler-house equipment.

take-off sheet

A form used for job cost calculations using information from the job specification and *scaled drawings*. The contractor produces costings for a tender by identifying the exact type of material and the amount required and the installation time and labour cost. This gives a total amount for the particular section of the job. Most large organisations use a computer software system for these calculations.

Item	Qty	Description	Init cost	Discount	Material cost £	Hours to install	Hourly rate £	Total labour £
1	200m	20mm galvanised conduit	1.2/m	0	240.00	70	9.50	665.00
2	30	Earthing couplings	.24	0	7.20	0	0	0
3	30	20mm std. brass bushes	.10	0	3.00	0	0	0
4	150	20mm distance saddles	.48	0	72.00	0	0	0
5	150	1.5 x 8 brass screw and plugs	.03	0	4.50	0	0	0

▲ Take-off sheet

A
B
C
D
E
F
G
H
I
J
K
L
M
N
O
P
Q
R
S
T
U
V
W
X
Y
Z

tangent

A mathematical function of an angle of a right-angled triangle, used in trigonometry. The tangent is the ratio of the length of side opposite the angle to the length of the adjacent side.

technical diagrams

Drawings which illustrate plans or work more easily than explaining them in words. Electrical drawings use symbols to BS EN 60617 standards.

See *Assembly drawing*; *Block diagram*; *Circuit diagram*; *Record (as fitted) drawing*; *Scaled drawings*; *Schematic diagram*; *Wiring diagram*

tender

A bid to secure a contract.

terminals

The types of terminals used for securing conductors in accessories are shown in the diagram.

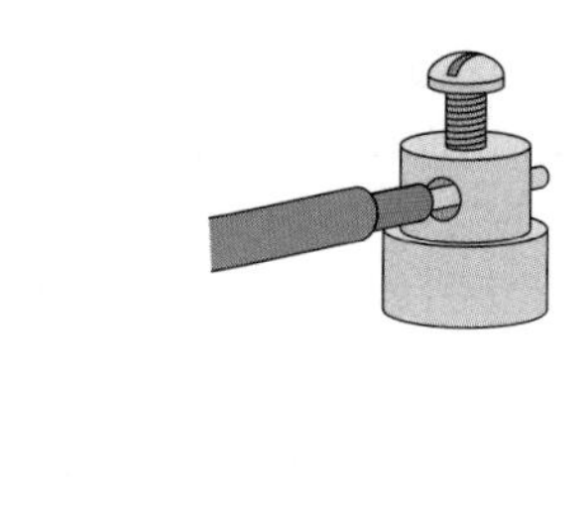

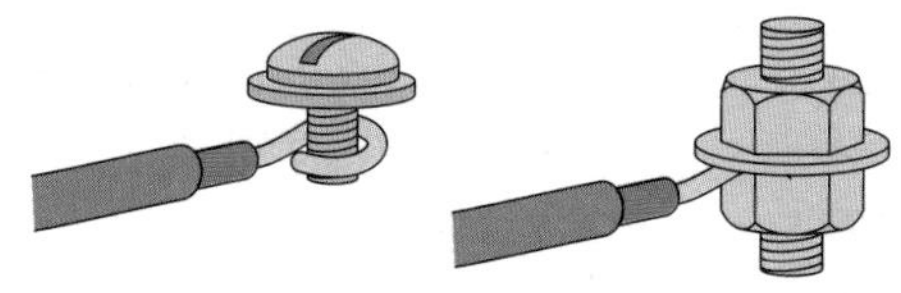

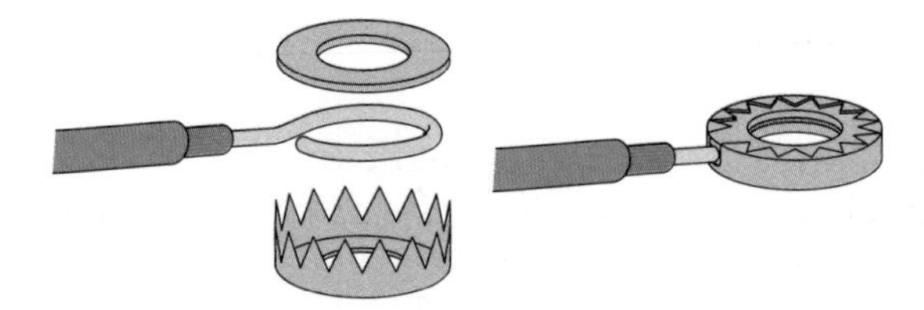

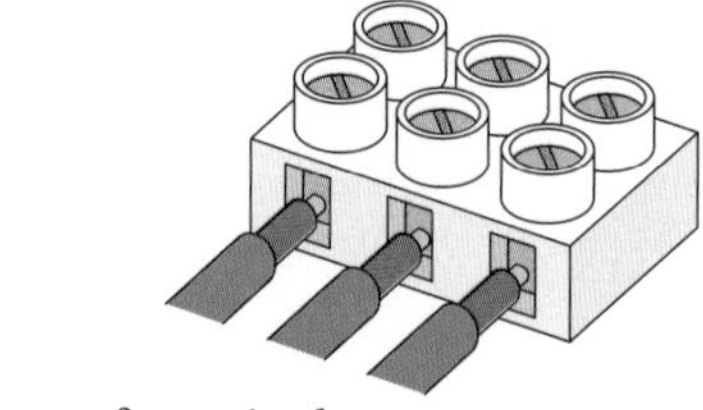

▲ Types of terminal

terminating cable

Cable terminations should anchor all the wires of a *conductor* securely, for example in a stranded conductor the strands should be twisted together before terminating. Some terminals should be crimped, for example for termination of bonding conductors to earth clamps and sink tops. When terminating flexible cords, the flex should be gripped with a flex clamp.

terminating conduit

Conduit may be terminated using a variety of methods, including: a conduit coupling and brass male bush; locknuts and a brass female bush; flanged coupling washer and brass male bush.

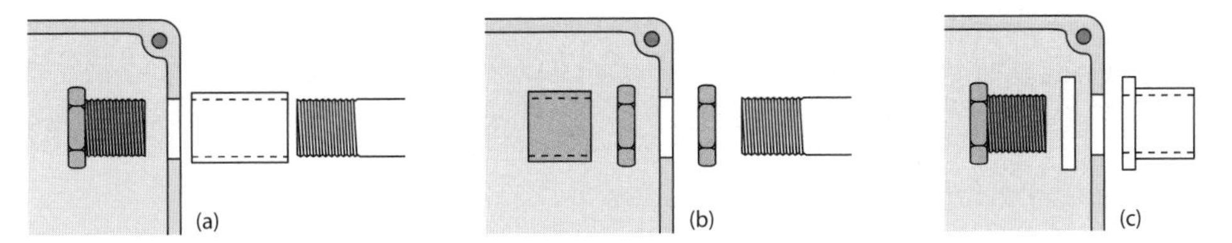

▲ (a) Terminating conduit at a box using a conduit coupling and brass male bush; (b) Terminating conduit at a box using locknuts and a brass female bush; and (c) Flanged coupling washer and brass male bush method for use with PVC box

test equipment

The safety requirements for electrical test instruments are covered in BS EN 61010. Electrical test equipment must have an up-to-date calibration certificate to prove that it provides accurate readings. To check test equipment regularly:

- inspect for damage, for example a broken casing may have resulted from an impact which could affect the readings
- ensure batteries are in good condition, of the same type and not leaking
- check that insulation on leads and probes is complete and secure
- check that the meter operates correctly with the leads open and short circuited, then zero the instrument on the ohm scale.

test lamp

An illuminated lamp used in a *voltage* indicating device. Test lamps may be a 15 W lamp or a series of *LEDs*. They should conform to the requirements of GS-38 Health and Safety guidance notes for test lamps.

test meter

A device for measuring *voltage* or *current*.

A B C D E F G H I J K L M N O P Q R S T U V W X Y Z

A
B
C
D
E
F
G
H
I
J
K
L
M
N
O
P
Q
R
S
T
U
V
W
X
Y
Z

thermal insulation

Thermal insulation prevents heat escaping from cables to the surrounding environment. Table 4A1 in the IEE Wiring *Regulations* provides a list of approved installation methods, and the five correction factors for thermal insulation must also be applied.

Correction factor	Tables for correction factor values	Symbol
Ambient temperature	Tables 4C1 & 4C2	Ca
Grouping factors	Tables 4B1, 4B2 and 4B3	Cg
Thermal insulation	Regulation 523-04-01	Ci
BS 3036 fuse	0.725 and Table 4C2	Cr
Mineral insulated cable	0.9 Table 4J1A	N/A

▲ Tables for correction factor values

thermal starter circuit

A starter for *fluorescent lamps* with four pins, two for the heater connection; it is not usually installed now, but is still found in many properties. The starter has closed contacts mounted on a *bi metallic strip*. There is a small heater coil which heats one contact when the supply is switched on. The strip bends and the contacts open, creating a momentary high voltage which starts the circuit discharge.

thermistor

A temperature-sensitive *resistor* used for measuring and controlling temperature up to 300°C, for example in motor windings and for sensing overloads. It is possible to connect the thermistor to the control circuit so that supply to the motor is cut when windings overheat. In a positive temperature coefficient (PTC) thermistor, the resistance increases with temperature increase; and *vice versa* for a negative temperature coefficient (NTC) thermistor. The rated resistance of a thermistor may be identified by the colour code shown in the table.

Colour	Resistance
Red	3,000 Ω
Orange	5,000 Ω
Yellow	10,000 Ω
Green	30,000 Ω
Violet	100,000 Ω

▲ Colour coding for rated resistance of thermistor

thermocouple

A temperature device which has two different metals bonded together with a lead for each one. A *voltage* is produced across the two leads when the metals are heated and the voltage increases with increased temperature. Thermocouples are used for measuring very high temperatures, such as in furnaces.

thermostat

A device that detects changes in temperature and switches a heater on or off at a pre-selected temperature setting. Some applications for a thermostat would be central heating systems, ovens, commercial ovens and processes, and anything else where there is a need to maintain a certain temperature.

See *Oven thermostats*; *Simmerstat*

three-phase a.c. synchronous motor

Synchronous motors are usually driven by transistorised variable-frequency drives. In the three-phase a.c. type, a squirrel-cage induction winding is added to the rotor to start the motor as an induction motor. Three-phase a.c. power is supplied to the stator causing a rotating *magnetic field* around the rotor which is then supplied with *d.c.* current through a field winding. The rotor then has north and south poles and is attracted to the rotating magnetic field producing a strong turning force on the rotor shaft.

three-phase induction motor

A three-phase supply connected to the stator has voltages 120° *out of phase*. The current then produces a moving *magnetic field* on the *stator* windings which induces a current in the *rotor*, creating a second magnetic field. This magnetic field, when combined with the first magnetic field from the stator windings, exerts a force on the conductors in the rotor causing it to turn.

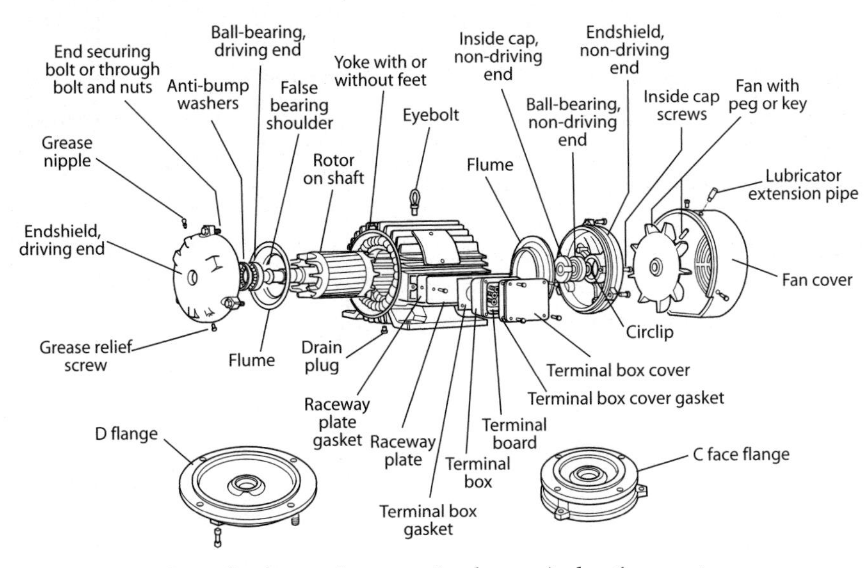

▲ Construction of a three-phase squirrel-cage induction motor

A B C D E F G H I J K L M N O P Q R S T U V W X Y Z

three-phase power

The power in a three-phase balanced load may be calculated using the formula:

$$\text{Power} = \sqrt{3} \times V_L \times I_L \times \cos \text{Ø}$$

For an unbalanced load, the power for each separate section must be calculated and then added.

See *Delta connection*; *Star connection*

three-phase rectifier circuits

These circuits provide a very smooth wave from the three-phase mains supply and are used to provide high-powered *d.c.* supplies. The rectifier circuit is created using six diodes connected as a three-phase bridge circuit.

three-phase supplies

The normal means of generating and transmitting electrical power, with each phase differing by 120°. Industrial users may operate directly from three-phase supplies. Domestic users are generally connected to one phase only, with total load on each phase balanced as closely as possible by the supplier. A three-phase circuit requires either three or four conductors connected in a star or delta connection.

See *Delta connection*; *Star connection*; *Transmission of electricity*

thyristor

Also called a silicon controlled rectifier (SCR), a thyristor is a semiconducting device with four layers of alternating n-type and p-type material. The anode and cathode cross four layers and the control terminal, or gate, is connected to a middle layer. The thyristor acts as a high-speed switch, and some, capable of switching MW of power, are used in high voltage direct current (HVDC) systems. The thyristor acts like a mechanical switch, and can be either on or off and nothing else.

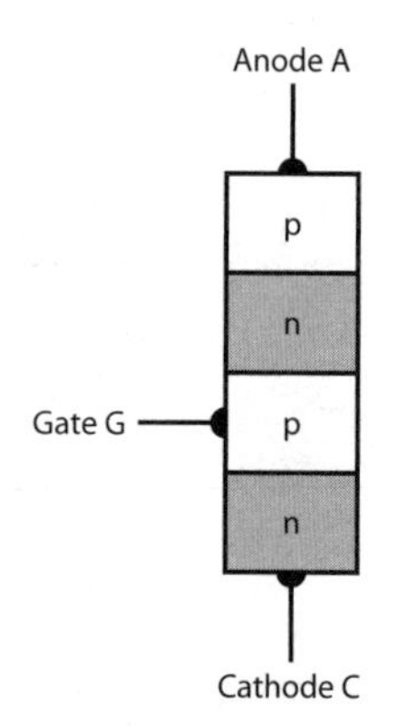

▲ Construction of a thyristor

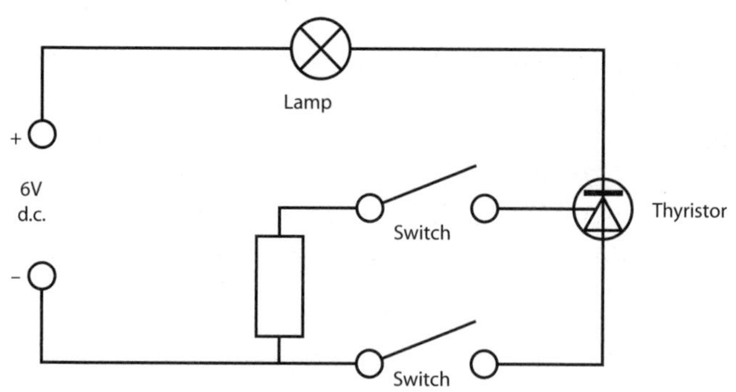

▲ Circuit for testing a thyristor

To test thyristors, a simple circuit is created, as shown in the diagram. The thyristor is operating correctly if: the lamp will not light when only switch B is closed; the lamp lights to full brilliance when switch A is also closed; the lamp remains illuminated when switch A is then opened.

timer

Standard timers are used to switch lights or heaters on and off. Complex programmable timers perform many different functions, for example a central-heating and hot-water programmer.

See *Programmer*

TN-C earthing system

An earthing system in which a single conductor combines the neutral and protective functions throughout the system. This system is restricted for specific situations and there must be no metallic connection between supply company equipment and the earthing system.

TN-C-S protective multiple earthing (PME) system

An earthing system in which a common conductor is used for the supply of neutral and earth, known as the protective earthed neutral (PEN) or combined neutral and earth (CNE) conductor. The combined supply conductor must be earthed at several points.

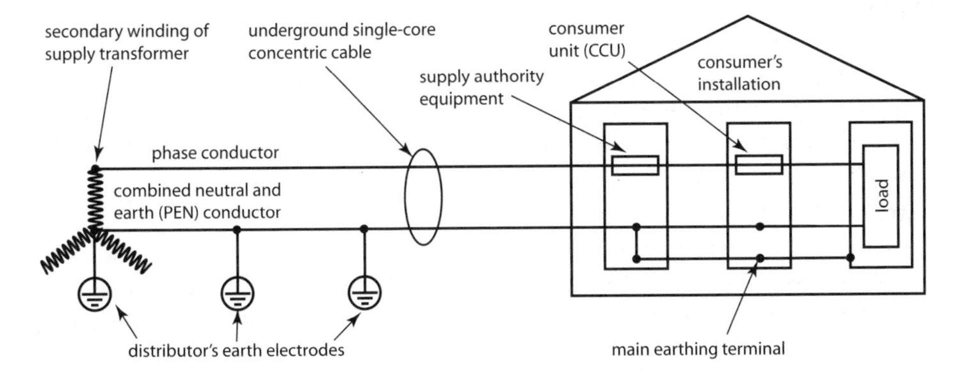

▲ TN-C-S, protective multiple earthing (PME) system

TN-S earthing system

An earthing system in which the earth is completely separate from the neutral, as opposed to the TN-C-S system. The earth return path is usually via the armouring of an SWA (steel wired armoured) cable or a lead sheaf on an older style supply cable.

A B C D E F G H I J K L M N O P Q R S T U V W X Y Z

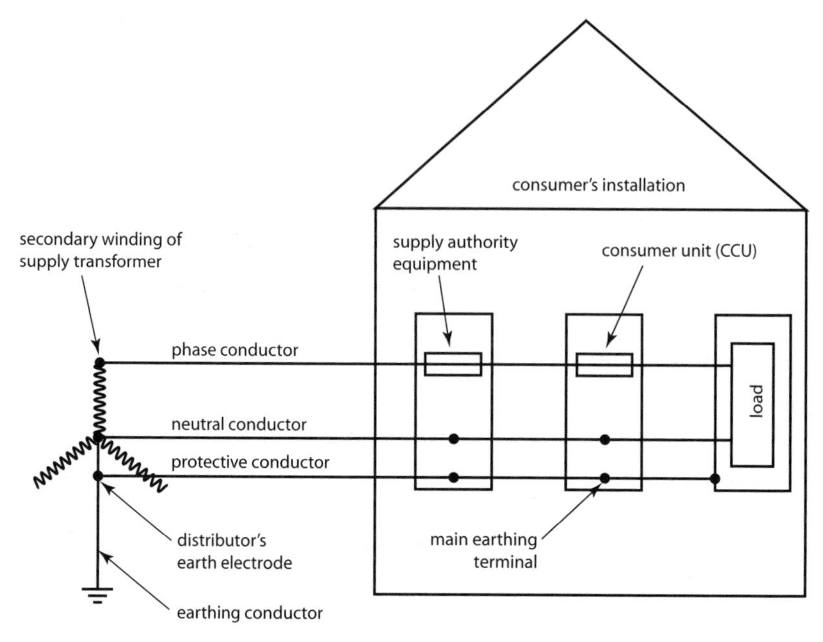

▲ TN-S earthing system with metallic earth return path

torque

A turning force, for example the force which causes the rotation of a motor.

toxic agents

Poisons which may cause injury and in some cases death, for example hydrogen cyanide. Always follow the instructions on Safety Data Sheets when dealing with any chemical.

trailing cables

Cables designed to withstand high levels of wear and tear. The strongest, most durable cables have heavy inner and outer sheathing and wire braid or flexible steel-wound armouring. The termination is usually made with couplers which can withstand bending. These cables may be used for robotic manufacturing equipment, and for heavy plant on construction sites, where the cables are trailed across the site and are therefore exposed to all weather conditions and may also have vehicles driven over them. Lighter trailing cable with heavy-duty rubber sheathing is used for equipment which is constantly moved, such as drills, where the cable must be able to withstand being scraped across the ground.

transformer

Electrical equipment used to transform *voltage* for distribution of electricity, construction work and for electronic applications. The voltage enters the transformer at the input level; a step-up transformer is used if the required output level is higher and a step-down transformer is used when the required output is lower.

See *Core-type transformer*; *Isolating transformer*; *Shell-type transformer*

transient voltage

A variation to the normal voltage causing the level to fall outside the range specified for the installation and equipment. Transient voltages may be caused by, for example, faults in the electricity supply or lightning strikes. Circuit conductors are designed to prevent voltage drops during normal circuit conditions, but transient voltages fall outside their range. Protective equipment, such as filters, can be installed, especially into IT circuits, to ensure stable voltage levels.

transistor

A *semiconductor* device used as a switch, or to allow *voltage* or *current* amplification. A bipolar transistor has three regions of semiconductor material: a pnp transistor with a central (base) n-type region and two outer p-type regions, the emitter and collector; and an npn transistor with a p-type central base and two n-type outer regions. On the diagrams, the arrow shows the direction of the flow of current.

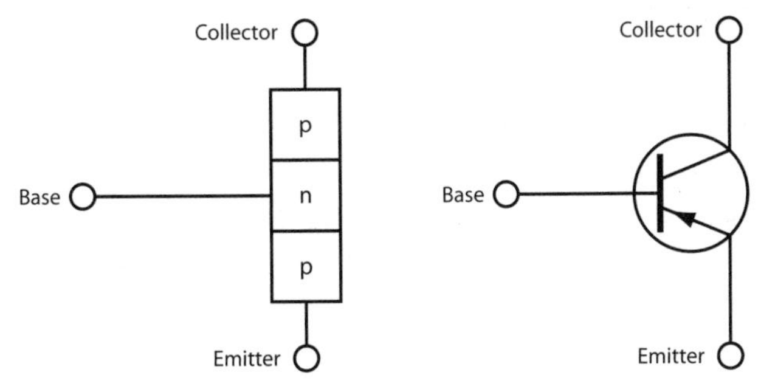

▲ pnp transistor and its associated circuit symbol

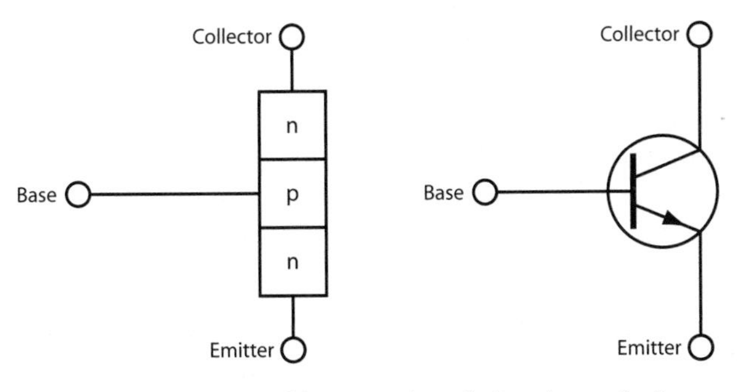

▲ npn transistor and its associated circuit symbol

A B C D E F G H I J K L M N O P Q R S T U V W X Y Z

Transistors will only operate when the base is thin with very few majority carriers and with the base-emitter junction forward biased and the base-collector junction reverse biased. To test transistors, meters with three terminals are used; an *ohmmeter* may be used to check correct conduction.

transmission of electricity

Electricity is transmitted at very high voltage over the *national grid* through steel-cored aluminium *conductors* suspended on steel pylons – the air acts as an *insulator* and coolant. Electricity is taken off the grid to sub-stations where the supply is transformed to 11 kV and distributed locally. Power station output is 25 kV and is transformed for transmission to:

- 400 kV and 275 kV – super grid
- 132 kV – original grid
- 66 kV and 33 kV – secondary transmission
- 11 kV – high-voltage distribution
- 415/400 V – commercial consumer supplies
- 240/230 V – domestic consumer supplies.

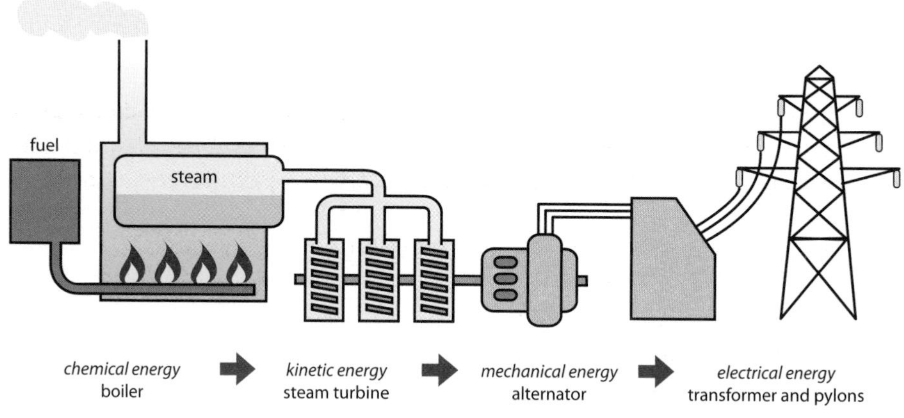

▲ The basic components of electricity generation systems

transposition

A mathematical method of arranging a formula or equation to find an unknown quantity. For example in *Ohms Law*, *voltage* (V) is equal to the *current* (I) multiplied by the *resistance* (R). The equation is written:

$$V = I R$$

Ohm's Law may be transposed to find the value of current:

$$\text{Current (I)} = \frac{\text{Voltage (V)}}{\text{Resistance (R)}}$$

And resistance:

$$\text{Resistance (R)} = \frac{\text{Voltage (V)}}{\text{Current (I)}}$$

triac/bidirectional thyristor

A *semiconductor* with three terminals used to control current. The triac is similar to a *thyristor* but has an inverse parallel connection and can control current in both directions.

true or active power

The power in a circuit which is used by the *resistor*(s). The *apparent power* in a resistive circuit is voltage (V) × current (I). The true power takes the phase angle (Ø) into account. It may be less than or equal to the apparent power and is calculated by the formula:
True power = VI cos Ø.

See *Apparent power*; *Power factor*; *Reactive power*

trunking

A rectangular casing for cables, sometimes having one side which allows access to the cable inside. The casing usually holds a number of cables following the same route or where equipment may be relocated frequently. Types of trunking include:

- square steel trunking with cover and coupling
- floor trunking
- multi-compartment trunking
- flush cable trunking
- overhead trunking
- skirting trunking
- busbar trunking.

(See diagrams overleaf)

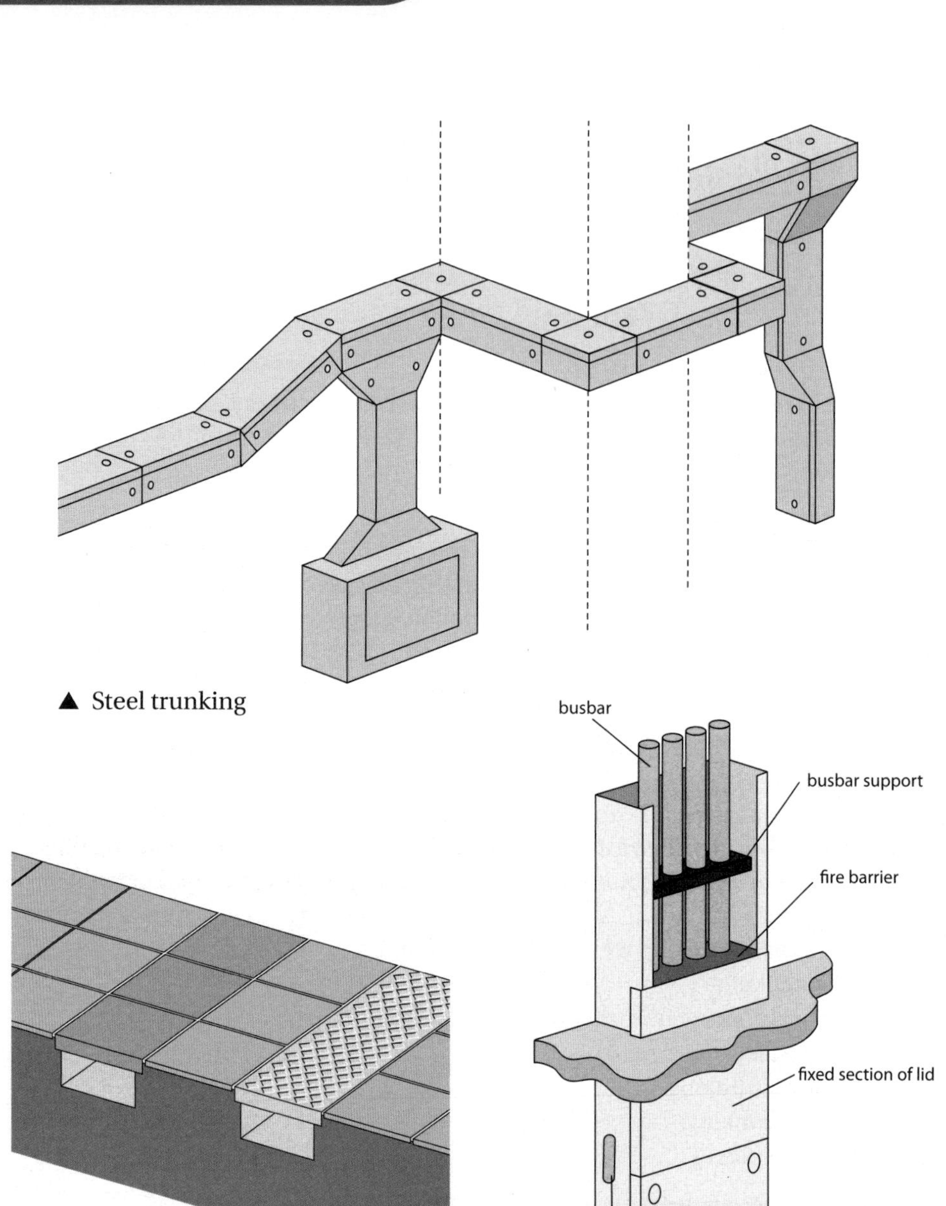

▲ Steel trunking

▲ Floor trunking

▲ Busbar trunking

TT system

An earthing system in which exposed metalwork is connected directly to earth using a separate earth electrode such as a copper rod.

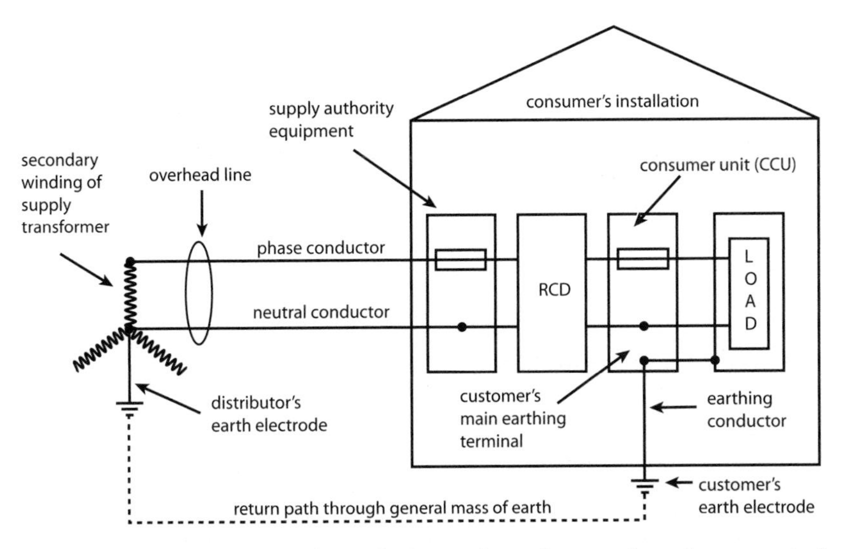

▲ Earthing with customer's earth electrode and ground earth return path

tubular heater

A type of radiant low-temperature heater which supplements the main heating. The tubular heater has a 50 mm mild steel or aluminium tube with a heating element mounted inside.

tungsten halogen lamp

A lamp with a tungsten filament enclosed in a quartz tube filled with argon and a controlled amount of a halogen gas such as iodine. The halogen allows the filament to be heated to a higher temperature than in an *incandescent lamp*, as it has a regeneration effect, so the lamp lasts longer. Two basic designs are double-ended linear and single-ended, the latter being used in the automotive industry for headlamp bulbs. The linear lamp must be installed within 4° of the horizontal. If the lamp is touched, the greasy deposit from the fingers could cause cracks in the quartz. To avoid this, clean the tube with methylated spirit before use.

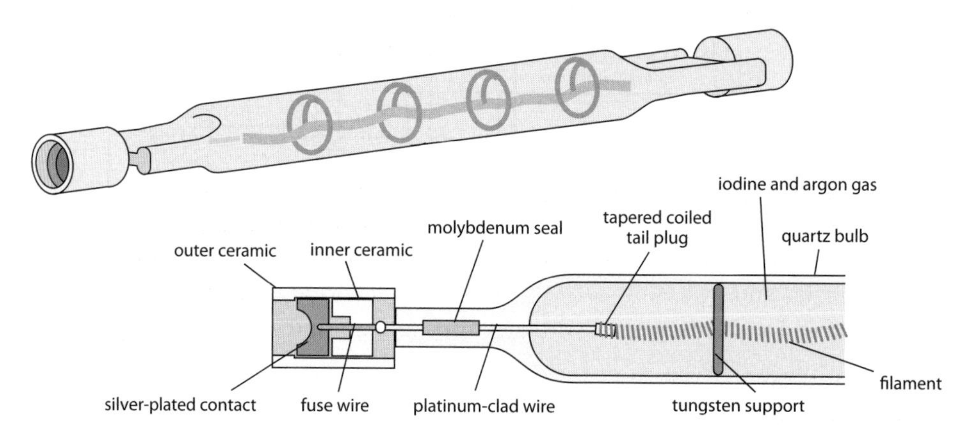

▲ Linear tungsten halogen lamp

two-pole voltage detector

See *Voltage detector/voltage indicating device*

type 'D' fuse

A fuse developed to European testing regulations and approved by all European testing authorities. This fuse is superseded by the *neozed fuse*, but is still present in older installations.

ultrasonic intruder alarm device

Ultrasonic device used with a 12 volt *d.c.* supply to protect buildings by sending out sound waves which bounce back to the device when no one is in the building. If a sound wave contacts an intruder, it is changed by deflection and causes the alarm to trigger.

See *Intruder alarm system*

under-voltage protection

See *No-volt protection*

underfloor heater

A type of heater, where the heating elements, made from materials such as aluminium, chromium, copper, silicon or manganese alloys, are installed under the floor and heat the tiles on the surface. The insulating materials used are also made from a variety of materials such as PVC, silicone rubber and nylon. Asbestos was also used for insulation and electricians should check for this before working on any existing underfloor installation.

See *Asbestos dust safety*

uninsulated connector

Connector for earth cables and protective conductors inside wiring panels and fuse boards.

uninterruptible power supply (UPS)

Standby electrical power used in small offices to protect computer systems from loss of data in the event of a *power* fault. The UPS is a *battery* supply charged by the mains when not in use and which cuts in automatically when there is a loss of power. The d.c. battery supply is electronically converted to a mains supply voltage which can support a network of computers.

A
B
C
D
E
F
G
H
I
J
K
L
M
N
O
P
Q
R
S
T
U
V
W
X
Y
Z

unity power factor

The unity power factor is a power factor of one (1.0). This occurs in a purely *resistive circuit* and all the current contributes to the power in the load.

See *Power factor*

valence electrons

The electrons orbiting furthest from the nucleus of an atom.

See *Semiconductors*

variable frequency drive (VFD)

A combination of a converter at the input, a constant voltage *d.c.* bus and an inverter at the output, used to create variable *a.c.* voltage and frequency for a motor. The converter has *diodes* in a bridge configuration and converts a.c. to d.c. supply. The constant-voltage d.c. bus filters and smoothes the d.c. voltage waveform and the inverter changes the d.c. back to a.c. with *insulated gate bipolar transistors (IGBT)*, creating a variable a.c. voltage and frequency output.

variable speed drive (VSD)

Used in *a.c. induction motors* to control the *voltage* and *frequency* supplied to the motor, producing variable speed. The control is produced by varying the frequency or the number of pole pairs, and by changing the applied voltage and armature resistance. The variable speed drive reduces the current for starting and allows more control over the *torque*.

variation order

A document created to record agreed changes to the contracted work for a project. This often happens when unforeseen circumstances extend the length of time a job will take. The document must be signed by the client before the extra work is started.

video switcher

A *CCTV* switcher used to change the observer's screen view between images from surveillance cameras one at a time, or to record the images to a VCR.

A B C D E F G H I J K L M N O P Q R S T U V W X Y Z

volt

The unit of *electromotive force (e.m.f.)* required to cause a flow of electric *current*. One volt is equal to one *joule/coulomb*.

volt-amps (VA)

The unit measurement of *apparent power* (VA).

voltage

The force available to push *current* around a circuit, or the difference in electrical potential between two points in a circuit.

See *Electromotive force*; *Potential difference*

voltage detector/voltage indicating device

An instrument used for detecting or measuring voltage. A detector may have a lamp or a meter scale and should be protected against excess current by a high breaking capacity *fuse* with a low current rating (less than 500 mA) or a current-limiting *resistor* and fuse. There are also detectors that use more than one indicator, as the energy input to the detector is limited by the circuitry used. For example, the two-pole voltage detector has an integral test probe, an interconnecting lead and a second test probe. Test lamps and voltage indicators should be marked with the maximum voltage that the device can test. Testing should ensure that the devices are not connected for longer than a few seconds.

voltage drop

A loss of electrical 'pressure' caused by the *resistance* in the *conductor* and components in a circuit – the longer the conductor (e.g. cable), the greater the voltage drop. The voltage drop in cable conductors is given in BS 7671 and manufacturers' data. Regulation 525-01-02 requires that the voltage drop between the supply terminals and a socket outlet should not be greater than 4 per cent.

voltage indicating device

See *Voltage detector/voltage indicating device*

voltmeter

An instrument used to measure *voltage*, the voltmeter measures the potential difference between two points and must be connected in parallel across the circuit. The internal *resistance* of a voltmeter has to be very high to produce accurate readings.

vulcanised butyl rubber (vulcanised India rubber)

An old-fashioned cable insulator that is no longer used because it becomes brittle with age and breaks up, exposing the conductor. It has been replaced by PVC insulation.

See *Synthetic rubber insulation*

Ward-Leonard speed control

A speed control for *d.c.* machines used in applications such as passenger lifts. The Ward-Leonard speed control involves the application of a *voltage* across the *armature* terminals which is lower than the rated voltage. This controls the field winding of a separate generator and provides a variable voltage to the armature terminals.

warning device

A device that indicates that there is a risk of danger. It could be a warning notice on a wall or door to an electrical installation, or a mechanical device that warns of electrical danger in a circuit such as a sounder, claxon or bell.

warning notice

A notice that indicates that there is a risk of danger ahead. The notice should be clearly visible and printed on a bright yellow background with a black border. Any equipment operating in excess of 250 volts should have a warning notice, especially when this level of voltage is not expected.

water heating system

A system for heating water. There are two main types of hot water system:

- instantaneous water heating which heats water as required
- hot water storage, which stores hot water ready for use.

In all types of water-heating system, storage or instantaneous, the exposed conductive parts must be bonded to earth and the cables should be the right size for the full load current.

See *Immersion heater*; *Instantaneous water heater*; *Thermostat*

A B C D E F G H I J K L M N O P Q R S T U V W X Y Z

watt

The unit of measurement of *true power*, P = VI cos Ø, measured by a *wattmeter*.

wattmeter

Instrument for measuring power in an *a.c.* circuit which contains *capacitance* or *inductance*. The illustration shows a wattmeter with a current coil wired in series with the load between W_1 and W_2, and a voltage coil wired in parallel across the supply between P_1 and P_2. This method will measure the power in a single-phase circuit or in a balanced three-phase load (in this case the total power will be three times the meter value).

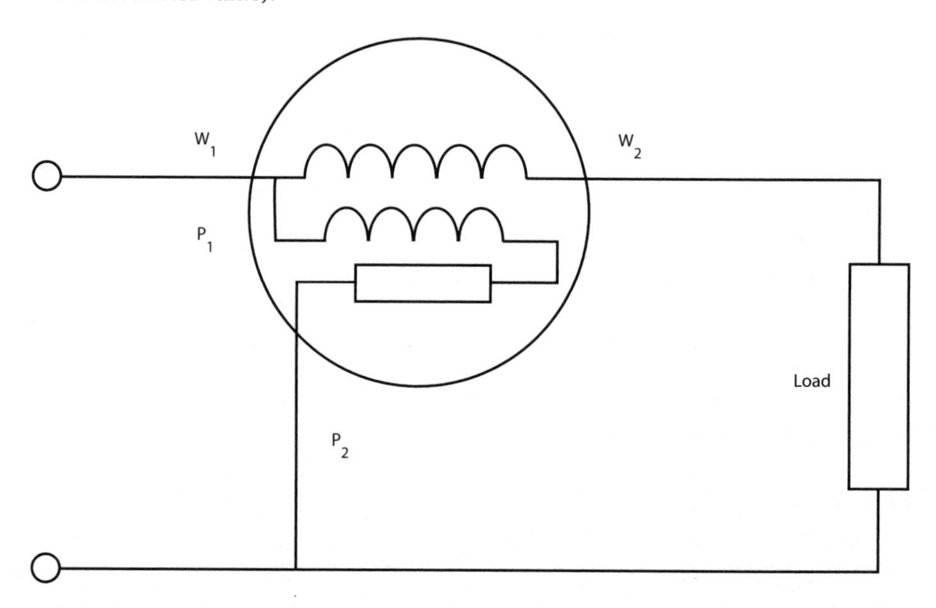

▲ Wattmeter connected to load

weight

The gravitational force pulling a body of material towards the ground.

windage

Physical resistance created by the air inside the casing of the rotating part of a motor or generator.

wiring diagram

A simplified diagram of the physical layout, components and connections in a circuit.

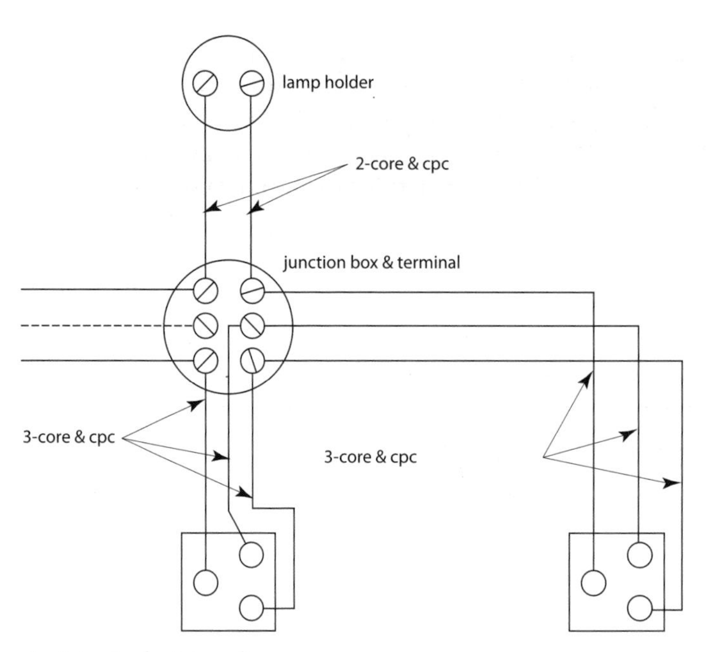

▲ A typical wiring diagram

wound rotor

A rotor in which the *conductors* form an internally *star-connected* three-phase winding with the other ends attached to slip rings on the shaft. The wound-rotor motor is used:

- to ensure that the starting *current* is not too high for the capacity of the *power* system
- for high-inertia loads with a long acceleration time
- for high-slip loads
- for adjustable speed installations which do not need precise control, such as conveyor belts, hoists and elevators.

(See diagram overleaf)

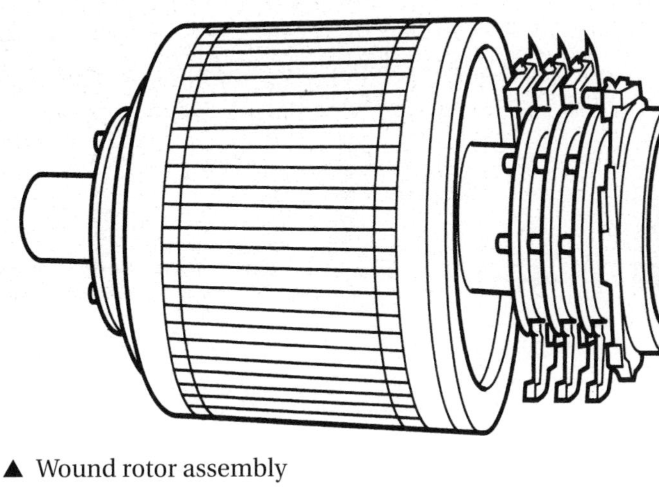

▲ Wound rotor assembly

xenon lamp

A light source containing xenon gas. The lamp emits a very bright light for its physical size and is an intense source of ultraviolet, visible and near-infrared light. It is usually operated as a pulsed light source, as in a strobe lamp, by electrical discharge in xenon under high pressure.

A
B
C
D
E
F
G
H
I
J
K
L
M
N
O
P
Q
R
S
T
U
V
W
X
Y
Z

yoke

Important component of every electric motor or generator. Essentially it is the frame to which magnets creating the *magnetic field* are attached, either *permanent magnets* or *electromagnets*. Its design plays a key part in the structure, performance and efficiency of the machine. It may be solid, made of conductive iron providing a flux path for the magnetic field and also acting as a heat sink to stop overheating. Alternatively, it may be in several parts, be laminated in steel or aluminium, and can be fixed or rotating.

zener diode

A *p-n junction* device designed to operate in the reverse breakdown region. The breakdown voltage, zener voltage (V_z), is set during manufacturing by precise doping and can produce tolerances to within 0.05 per cent. A reverse-biased zener diode exhibits a controlled breakdown, allowing current to flow and maintaining the zener voltage across the diode. A zener diode is connected in parallel across a load to act as a voltage limiting or regulation device. To limit voltage from a variable voltage source to a known value, the zener diode is connected reverse biased in parallel and acts as a short circuit when the voltage reaches the diode's reverse-breakdown voltage. This application of the zener diode is called a shunt voltage regulator.

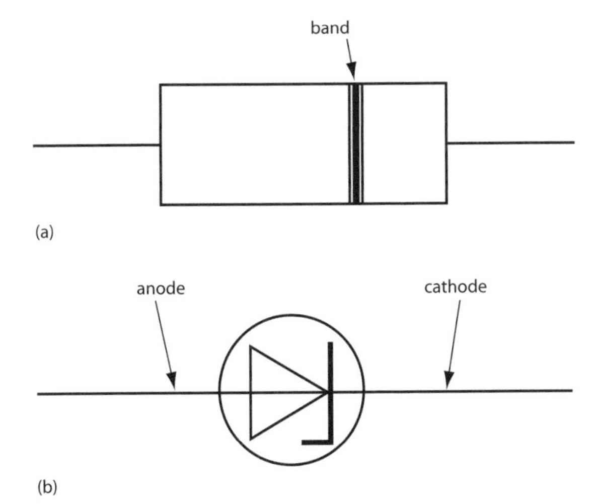

▲ Zener diode characteristics

zero phase angle

In a resistive circuit the voltage and current pass through maximum and zero at the same time as each other. The voltage and current are in phase with each other and have a zero phase angle between them.

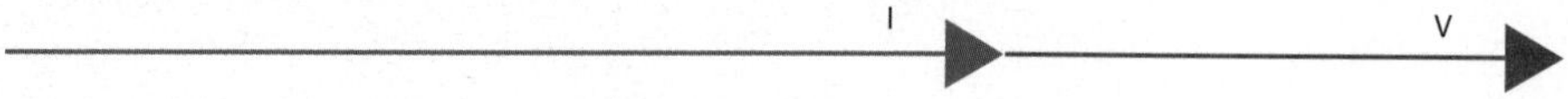

I V

▲ Phasor diagram for zero phase angle